The
Delicate
Balance

Best wishes

Printed in Colombia

The Delicate Balance

Coming Catastrophic Changes

On Planet Earth

by John Zajac

Prescott Press, Inc.
P. O. Box 53788
Lafayette, LA 70505
(318) 237-7049

Special thanks are extended to Kathy Ceraso, without whose professionalism and expert editing this book would be a collection of incomprehensible thoughts.

Grateful acknowledgment is made to the publishers and copyright holders named below for permission to reprint the material contained in this book.

Excerpt from *Kissinger: The Adventures of Super-Kraut* by Charles R. Ashman. Copyright 1972 by Charles R. Ashman. Reprinted by permission of Lyle Stuart, Inc., 120 Enterprise Avenue, Secaucus, NJ.

Excerpt from *Computers and the Beast of Revelation* by David Webber and Noah Hutchings. Copyright 1986 by David Webber and Noah Hutchings. Reprinted by permission of Huntington House, Inc., P.O. Box 53788, Lafayette, LA.

Excerpt from *How To Prepare for the Coming Crash* by Robert L. Preston. Copyright 1971, 1975 by Robert L. Preston. Reprinted by permission of Hawkes Publishing, Inc., P.O. Box 15711, Salt Lake City, UT.

Excerpt from *The New American*, "Abolish the Fed," by Alan Stang. Copyright 1985 by The New American. Reprinted by permission of The New American, 395 Concord Avenue, Belmont, MA.

Excerpt from *U.S. News & World Report* editorial "The Morning After" by Harold Evans. Copyright 1986 by *U.S. News & World Report*. Reprinted by permission of *U.S. News & World Report*, 2400 N Street, N.W., Washington, DC.

Graphic Acknowledgments

Sincere thanks are extended to owners of the following copyrighted graphics used in this publication. Permission has been granted for all reproductions, and all rights are reserved. Drawings and photographs not otherwise noted are from the author's private library.

Cover.   Altered picture of Earth. By courtesy of the Jet Propulsion Laboratory/National Aeronautics and Space Administration.

Figure II-1.   Painting titled *George Washington* by Charles Willson Peale (1787). Reprinted by permission of The Pennsylvania Academy of the Fine Arts, Philadelphia, PA. Bequest of Mrs. Sarah Harrison (the Joseph Harrison, Jr., Collection).

Figure IV-1.   Great Orion Nebula, M-42. Courtesy of the Jet Propulsion Laboratory/National Aeronautics and Space Administration.

Figure IV-2.   Viking photograph of the cratered terrain of Mars. By courtesy of the Jet Propulsion Laboratory/National Aeronautics and Space Administration.

Figure IV-3.   Photograph from *The Oakland Tribune*. Reprinted by permission of *The Oakland Tribune*, Oakland, CA.

Figure IV-4a.   Photograph from Saltair Resort. Reprinted by permission of Saltair Resort, 87 South, 350 East, North Salt Lake City, UT.

Figure IV-5.   Illustration from ABC News "Smog in Mexico City." Copyright 1988 by the American Broadcasting Company. Reprinted by permission of the American Broadcasting Company, 30 Rockefeller Center, New York, NY.

Figure IV-8.   Illustration from the U.S. Department of the Interior. Reprinted by permission of the U.S. Geological Survey Library, Menlo Park, CA.

Figure IV-9.   Photograph from the Bancroft Library. Reprinted by permission of the Bancroft Library, University of California at Berkeley.

Figure V-3b and V-4.   Photographs from *Baedeker's Egypt* by Karl Baedeker. Copyright by Karl Baedeker. Reprinted by permission of Karl Baedeker GmbH, Stuttgart, West Germany.

Note: Every effort has been made to locate the copyright owners of material used in this book. Omissions brought to our attention will be corrected in subsequent editions.

Graphic Acknowledgments

Sincere thanks are extended to all from whom the following copyrighted graphics used in this publication. Permission has been granted for all reproductions, and all rights are reserved. Drawings and photographs not otherwise noted are from the author's private library.

Cover   Altered picture of Earth, as courtesy of the Jet Propulsion Laboratory, National Aeronautics and Space Administration.

Figure 1-1   Painting titled *Decay of Pennsylvania* by Charles Willson Peale (1787). Reproduced by permission of The Pennsylvania Academy of the Fine Arts, Philadelphia, PA. (Bequest of Mrs. Sarah Harrison, the Joseph Harrison Jr. Collection.)

Figure 1-1   Chart of HLM?/Sphinx, M.D. Congress of the U.S. Population Radiology, National Aeronautics and Space Administration.

Figure 1-2   Altha photograph of the capsized remains of Mars, the courtesy of the 18/?, Population Laboratory, National Aeronautics and Space Administration.

Figure 1?-2 Photograph? Drawing. Oakland? County. Reprinted by permission of the Oakland Tribune, Oakland, CA.

Figure 1-2   Placemats from Sillan Resort. Reprinted by permission on the Salton Resort, 57 South 3rd East North Salt Lake City, UT.

Figure 1-?   Illustration from *ABC News "Sting* in Mexico City Corps, hosted by the American Broadcasting Company. Reprinted by permission of the American Broadcasting Company, © Rockefeller Center, New York NY.

Figure? 1-? Illustration from the U.S. Department of the Interior. Reprinted by permission of the U.S. Geological Survey Library, Menlo Park, CA.

Figure 1?-? Photograph from the Bancroft Library. Reprinted by permission of the Bancroft Library, University of California at Berkeley.

Figure? 1-? Photographs from *Readers Digest* © copyright by Karl Baedeker. Copyright by Karl Baedeker. Reprinted by permission of Karl Baedeker GmbH, Stuttgart, West Germany.

Note: Every effort has been made to locate the copyright owners of material used in this book. Omissions brought to our attention will be corrected in subsequent editions.

CONTENTS

CONTENTS

I. INTRODUCTION

The world we take for granted depends on a delicate balance of conflicting forces—a balance endangered every day of modern life. Throughout the world, mankind has learned to live with the constant threat of nuclear war and human extinction. Economic fluctuations at home or in remote corners of the world can have a disastrous impact on society. Environmental problems point out the urgent need for global cooperation and action. As we attempt to make long range plans, we are increasingly plagued by uncertainties.

What lies ahead? Can modern science unlock the mysteries of the future? As science challenges the mind, what happens to the human spirit? Can each of us determine our own fate, or are we part of a larger scheme beyond our control?

Contrary to popular opinion, science and religion need not be diametrically opposed. Both science and theology can help us understand our future. The high technology of modern science provides tools for understanding and substantiating predictions made by both religious and secular figures. If one can know the future, then there is an order to the universe, however frightening that future may be.

The following chapters raise many questions as they present evidence of what the future holds. The journey begins with prophesies to test the validity of past and future predictions. The next step is explanations of how these predictions may come to pass in terms of political, economic, and environmental events. Finally, the discussion turns to the larger picture: what it all means. Evidence of the delicate balance and the forces affecting it invite you to draw your own conclusions.

II. THE PROPHETS:
Washington,
Nostradamus, and John

As unlikely as their brotherhood may seem, George Washington, Michael Nostradamus, and St. John the Apostle all shared something unique: They were able to see far into the future. Understanding what they saw and appreciating the improbability of their accuracy concerning events so far in the future is entertaining. However, if history establishes that their "visions" about our past were accurate, then what they foresaw in our future becomes highly relevant. Prophesies from each of these three men, who represent vastly different walks of life, have come true. Learning what may be our future and comprehending the cause and purpose of such visions have significance far beyond entertainment.

WASHINGTON

It does not seem possible to study Washington without first considering our nation's early history, a turn of events that may surprise some people. If you ask anyone who was the first President of the United States, the answer would certainly be George Washington. But take a moment to examine this long-held belief to see if it is true.

When was the United States declared a country? Everyone agrees that happened on July 4, 1776. However, America had already formed the second Continental Congress and an army, which fought the British at the Battle of Lexington and Concord a year and three months earlier on April 18, 1775. Although America may have been acting as a nation in 1775, the formal declaration came in July 1776; therefore, we celebrated our 200th anniversary as a nation in 1976. By definition, the President of the country is the Chief Presiding Officer of the Federal Government. There has never been any disagreement that only one United States of America has existed.

George Washington was a general who fought in the Revolutionary War for six years. Was he President during the time that he was general? No. Was there a United States of America? Sure. There was a Continental Congress, a constitution called the Articles of Confederation, and a President, who presided over the Continental Congress. George Washington did not even consider being Chief Executive Officer of the Federal Government until after the Constitution of the United States was ratified. The Constitution was drafted in 1782, signed in 1788, and enacted in 1789. Well, then who was the first President of the United States?

The first President of the Continental Congress, and therefore of the United States, was John Hancock.[*] George Washington was the first President of the United States under the U.S. Constitution, which was ratified 12 years after the establishment of the United States of America.

It may now be of little consequence who actually was the first President of the United States. What is important about this discussion is our ability to examine new approaches to old, comfortable beliefs without bias and then to make an intelligent, objective decision. Many of us become so accustomed to some basic beliefs that we never question their origin or truth.

Examining the birth date of America raises the possibility that we celebrated the Bicentennial of the United States too soon. If Washington was the first President, then the anniversary was inaccurate. If the anniversary was right, then Washington was not the first President of the United States. We are living with this inaccuracy because most people admire George Washington and think John Hancock only wrote insurance.

---

[*]The first day that America was declared an independent nation was July 4, 1776. Original documents preserved in the National Archives Building in Washington, DC, show that even the first documents of the United States were signed "John Hancock, President."

George Washington was more than just a general and a President; he became the focus of many myths and misconceptions. For example, Washington did not have wooden teeth. If you think about the weakness of wet wood, you will understand why teeth could not be made of wood. He had calf's teeth, which closely resembled human teeth. Also, he never chopped down a cherry tree. And he tried to join the British Army as an officer but was turned down (before the Revolutionary War) for lack of formal British military schooling.

It has also been reported that he swore quite profoundly and never ate a grapefruit (it was not yet created). George Washington was one of the few people to own a buffalo, and he was the first person in America to breed mules. Although we celebrate Washington's birthday February 22, George's actual day of birth was on February 11 because he was born before the introduction of the Gregorian (modern) calendar.*

Other things not widely known about George Washington are more significant. Certainly, he was our greatest leader, fully deserving of the title "Father of Our Country." He could not have earned this title had he not survived the many battles he fought before being elected President. His early survival is worthy of mention because unlike his peers, Washington was conspicuous during combat—riding about continuously while checking the lines and giving orders and encouragement to his men. Since commanders and generals were prime targets at battlefronts, many of them would safely watch their battles from a secure position, such as a hilltop, well behind their lines. Although their remoteness protected them, it also prevented them from communicating and building troop morale.

---

*England finally adapted the Gregorian calendar in 1752, when Washington was 20 years old. The modern calendar corrected past inaccuracies by dropping 11 days. It also moved New Year's Day from March 25 to January 1.

Figure II-1. George Washington

During one of these battles—the Braddock Campaign of the French and Indian War—two horses were shot from under Washington as he led his troops in combat. Of course, the enemy was not aiming at the horses. Furthermore, the jacket that Washington wore in that battle was pierced by four bullets, some of which made multiple holes.[1] But Washington did not have a cut, scrape, or scratch on him. One could argue that he hung his jacket on a fence post, and someone used it for target practice, and the two horses just broke their legs and really were not shot. Still, there are other possibilities. For example, this phenomenon could be tied to a supernatural experience that Washington had at Valley Forge.

This experience, which occurred during the gravest point of the Revolutionary War, greatly affected Washington. Valley Forge in the winter of 1777–1778 was a trying time for the United States, Washington, and his army. His troops did not have enough to eat, they could not keep warm, and they almost lost the war to the British. This was a war that was unthinkable in the first place. Never before had a colony dared to defy its king. Small wonder that Washington was considering the terms of surrender. What stopped him from giving up at Valley Forge? Washington spoke about being visited one afternoon by an Angelic Being.

According to Washington, what he described as a beautiful, Angelic Being appeared in his tent and said to him, "Son of the Republic, take heed, and learn."[2] Then the Angelic Being presented a vision to him in which he saw a great war, the Revolutionary War, with the British being defeated. He saw the birth of a great nation that grew and prospered and expanded across the continent. He also saw an Angelic Being with a golden crown on his head on which was written the word Union. Incidentally, the term "Union" was never written in the Declaration of Independence or the Continental Congress or any part of the Congress when Washington saw this vision. Yet, of course, the Union is a key point in the Constitution, which was in part written with George Washington.

The Angelic Being then said, "Son of the Republic, the end of the century cometh, look and learn."[2] Presumably, the Angelic Being was referring to the nation's century not the calendar century. In the second vision, Washington saw the North fighting the South, with great bloodshed and violence. He saw that the North won, that it rebuilt the South, and that America remained one nation, growing larger and stronger. He saw great cities spring up across the nation.

And a third time the Angelic Being said, "Son of the Republic, take heed, and learn."[2] He saw water being scooped up out of the sea and poured over Europe, Asia, and Africa. A large, black cloud developed (a symbol of war), and great fighting took place. And then, suddenly, America was engulfed by black smoke and flame. He saw that the cities of America were burned and devastated. The only people left were in the countryside.

Finally, across the Atlantic Ocean came people from Europe and Asia, and they invaded America on the eastern coast. He saw that the American people could not endure against this invasion. Finally, all were in despair, the whole country was overrun by the enemy, and most Americans were killed or were hiding in the hills. Then Washington saw angels with drawn swords coming down from the heavens to drive back the invaders. The Angelic Being then said, "Heed and beware, for all of the nations of the Earth gathered against her will not prevail."[2]

The three wars that Washington saw were the only ones that could have destroyed America. The Revolutionary War was almost lost. In fact, except for Washington's tenacity and Benjamin Franklin's diplomacy in making the English think that the French were going to support America more strongly, the war would indeed have been lost. Washington saw the Civil War, which could very well have destroyed America by dividing the nation.

Political scientists substantiate a flaw in the plan of many early Americans to merge Canada and the United States. The early Americans actually started a war (the motives of which are conveniently left out of most school books) to take over Canada by force, which, obviously, failed. If America had succeeded, the country would have grown too large too quickly, precluding a unified nation because of difficulties in communication, transportation, and economics. The French-speaking people living in Canada and the many British Loyalists who fled the Revolutionary War would not have easily merged into a new English-speaking, independent nation. Such a nation would most likely not have succeeded.

Similarly, if the South had not been defeated in the Civil War, embitterment would have left a weak Confederacy and a weak Union that would have been uncooperative and mutually antagonistic for many years. The lack of a strong, unified nation probably would have resulted in additional fragmentation, especially with the future formation of the western territories, which may have become small, independent nations such as Texas once was. Thus, the results of the Civil War could have destroyed America as a country and denied the fragmented parts a position as a world power.

The last war that Washington saw could only be described as World War III which, according to Washington, will be so devastating as to require divine intervention for America to survive. Of course, in the last 40 years the complete destruction of nations through nuclear war has become a genuine concern to us all.

Can prophets tell us what the future may hold? George Washington was definitely correct about the outcome of the Revolutionary War. He was right about the timing and the outcome of the Civil War. Time will tell if he was accurate about WWIII.

NOSTRADAMUS

Nostradamus was a popular prophet (though not in the Biblical sense), who lived in France during the sixteenth century. He was well educated in the sciences, especially in math, medicine, and astronomy.* He was well educated in the sciences, especially in math, medicine, and astronomy. He also studied French, Greek, Latin, Hebrew, Plato, and Socrates. His father was born into the Jewish faith, and his mother was a devout Christian. He was very much in support of the Bible, especially the Book of Revelation. He was also a noted physician, who would have been famous purely based on that reputation. Although Nostradamus could see the future, he wrote about it in disguise because he lived in a time of strong superstition and witch-hunts. So, Nostradamus composed poetry in quatrains and divided them into 10 groups or centuries (not related to time). Of these 10 groups or major chapters, nine and one-half were published in the sixteenth century. Although a reported eleventh and twelfth century were written, no one had seen the two remaining sets of predictions until recently.

Many scholars of Nostradamus claim that 50 to 80 percent of his predictions have already come true. For instance, Nostradamus predicted the exact date when his body would be dug up.[3] He did not tell anybody the date because doing so would have guaranteed that someone would force the prediction to come true. Instead, he predicted that whoever dug him up would soon see his own future: immediate death (Century IX, Quatrain 7).

Some drunken gentlemen decided that they would dig up Nostradamus after he had been buried over 200 years. Only bones remained in the grave, but the one who uncovered him was justifiably frightened, for around Nostradamus' neck was a brass plate placed there at the time of his death that read May 1793. The men were awed by the plaque with the current date. Immediately upon opening the doors to leave the church in which Nostradamus' body was entombed, the man who first uncovered the grave was killed by a random shot during the French Revolution.

---

*Nostradamus is often miscalled an astrologer because he stated the timing of future events by referring to the coincident position of heavenly bodies. However foreseeing changes in the calendar, he simply chose to use science to mark off historical events.

Figure. II-2 Nostradamus

Nostradamus also predicted the birth and significance of people such as Louis Pasteur and Montgolfier (inventor of the hot air balloon), including the dates of their most famous discoveries. Nostradamus was a unique physician, able to cure the plague without succumbing to it himself.[4] One might speculate if he saw into the future and recognized the value of penicillin and although started administering it, chose not to publicize its use as the inventor had not yet been born.

But Nostradamus was mostly known for seeing into the future. For instance, he wrote about a French king (Henri II) who would have his eye plucked out and would be killed while jousting. When Queen Catherine demanded to know if he was referring to her king, Nostradamus answered that he just wrote what he saw. She asked if Nostradamus was aware that the king did not joust. Nostradamus replied that he knew and that as long as the king did not joust, she had nothing to fear. The quatrain that Nostradamus wisely avoided giving a direct answer to was I-35:

> *The young lion shall overcome the old,*
> *In a warlike arena in single duel.*
> *In a golden cage his eye will be punctured,*
> *One of two types [of wounds], then to die a painful death.*

Two years later at a royal double wedding, Henri II was challenged to joust and could not refuse without embarrassment. So he entered a jousting tournament against the captain of the Scottish guard. Captain Montgomery was notably younger than the king, and he wore a similar emblem, a lion. On their third attempt to determine a victor, the contestants' lances shattered. Splintered fragments of Montgomery's weapon wounded the king in the neck, lifted his gold colored visor and penetrated his eye and skull. Henri's suffering continued for 10 days until his death. Coincidence?

Nostradamus also wrote of the formation and duty of America. He referred to America as the "New Land." He said the New Land would be born of the Britannic Island 15 years before her "brother" and that through "promise and truth" she shall preserve the balance (Quatrain IV-96). Few could argue against America's promise of liberty being instrumental in keeping the balance of power through two world wars and preventing a third. The French were the first to recognize America as a nation and were her strongest ally during the American Revolution. The French Revolution started with the storming of the Bastille on July 14, 1789, 15 years after the formation of the First Continental Congress on September 5, 1774, exactly as Nostradamus predicted 234 years earlier.

Nostradamus said that during the French uprising 500 would swarm the tileworks (Quatrain IX-34). But there was no such place at the time of his predictions. Eventually, a palace was built on a site that previously had been occupied by tile kilns and thus became known as the "Tileworks." In addition, the crowd (which numbered many thousands) that stormed the Tileworks was known as "The Group of 500" because it originally had 500 members. This quatrain also foretold who (with very close spelling) would betray the king–before "Nabbon(ne)" and "Sau(l)ce" were even born. Count Nabbonne became the scheming Minister of War to Louis XVI, and Sauce became the Mayor of Varennes who had Louis arrested.

Nostradamus was able to foresee many future events in his homeland of France. He said that during the Revolution King Louis XVI would flee Paris by coach, taking a peculiar route while in disguise as a monk (Quatrain IX-20). The route described was indeed the road the disguised king took with his wife, Marie Antoinette, who dressed like a nun. Nostradamus further wrote that they would be discovered. In Quatrain IX-77, he said that the queen would be tried by a jury chosen by lot and that the king's mistress would suffer the same fate as the queen. Louis XVI and Marie Antoinette were tried separately and were found guilty of treason. The queen's jurors were chosen by lot, a practice that was unknown in Nostradamus' day. The sentence for the king and queen was the guillotine—the same fate suffered by Mme. du Barry, who had been the mistress of kings. Trial by jury chosen by lot had never happened to royalty up to that time, and certainly the beheading of royalty was unthinkable in the 1500s. Overthrown royalty had been banished from the country, but had never been beheaded.

Nostradamus foresaw more than France and the near future or (as we see it) our past. He made predictions about future centuries. In many instances, he talked about what he called the three great Antichrists.

The first of these was Napoleon who was not identified by name. Instead, Napoleon was referred to as a great French king who would come from "short coat to long" (Quatrain VIII-57), in other words, from peasantry to emperor. He was to have a name like no other French king before him and "pay great attention to foreign women" (Quatrain IV-54). Nostradamus said that this king would have "short hair" and that he would reign for 14 years (Quatrain VII-13).

Napoleon did have uncustomarily short hair and did pursue women beyond the borders of France. As emperor, Napoleon enjoyed total power from November 1799 until April 1814–a total of 14 years and five months. Nostradamus predicted that Napoleon would be put in exile on a small island (Elba) (Quatrain I-32), and that after a short time, he would attempt a great comeback (Quatrain I-23). That would be when the "boar," which is what Napoleon was known as, would meet the "leopard," and the leopard would have his way with him in the third month. Although he had superior forces, Napoleon was defeated by the

Duke of Wellington, known as the leopard, at the Battle of Waterloo* on June 18, 1815, during the third month of his second campaign.†

Nostradamus did not often mention people by name. But for WWII, he named Franco: "From the house of Franco...shall cause confusion, fighting [civil war]...and shall deny entry to the great gulf [Mediterranean]" (Quatrain IX-16). Francisco Franco was the highest ranking insurgent of the Spanish Civil War, and he thus became Generalissimo (Chief General) after the war. On February 12, 1941, Franco refused permission for the Axis forces to pass through Spain to attack Gibraltar on the Mediterranean.

Nostradamus also named the second Antichrist, though he misspelled the name: "Liberty will not be regained...a fierce wicked villain...Hister..."(Quatrain V-29). A more definite description with a less accurate spelling is found in Quatrain II-24: "Ister [Hitler]...the native of Germany observes nothing [sacred]." And in Quatrain VI-49, "he shall overcome the borders of the Danube, and seek no justice but the twisted iron cross." The twisted iron cross accurately describes the swastika, and Hitler's expansions did overcome the borders of the Danube. The Danube River originates in southwestern Germany and flows through Austria, Czechoslovakia, Hungary, Yugoslavia, and

---

*The outcome of sixteenth century battles depended largely on the size of the combatant armies. Napoleon so anxiously sought the smaller British army that he split his forces with his next in command, General Grouchy, to increase his search area. The Duke of Wellington would have preferred delaying confrontation because Napoleon outnumbered his 75,000–man army by 25,000 men. Wellington had hoped to join forces with the Prussian Army under Marshal Von Blücher. Blücher, however, had been delayed by battle at Ligny. On June 18th, Napoleon's army found and attacked the British army, and as the day of battle approached an end, Wellington was all but totally defeated. Because of a lack of communications (not even signal fires were used), the locations of the second armies were unknown, and when the dust of an approaching army was seen, it was believed by both sides to be Grouchy's men. Instead, it was Blücher's 125,000–man army, which quickly snatched victory from the jaws of defeat. Although the events of the day became known to the combatants only when they occurred, Nostradamus gave an accurate accounting hundreds of years earlier.

†The second campaign started with the formation of Napoleon's new army.

Rumania. It runs along the borders of Bulgaria and Russia before it reaches the sea. After spending time in prison and then losing a presidential election, Hitler was appointed Chancellor and later took over as Supreme Dictator of Germany. He subsequently conquered Austria, Czechoslovakia, Hungary, and Yugoslavia. Rumania and Bulgaria joined with his forces, and he invaded Russia and advanced as far as Moscow and Leningrad.

The Germans took such delight in this prediction that they printed and airdropped leaflets all over France. The leaflets claimed that Nostradamus had been right about everything the Führer had done. The Germans pointed out that Nostradamus had predicted Germany would take over France and asked the French, "Why fight it?" By and large, they did not. Paris was occupied; it was not fought over. To this day, the British have not forgiven the French for failing to defend themselves.

The obvious question is: Did Nostradamus also predict that Hitler would lose? Yes, he did, but the Germans did not quote that part of his predictions.

Nostradamus, like many present-day historians, blamed the failure of the League of Nations at Lake Geneva for WWII (Quatrain I-47):

> *The talks of Lake Leman [Geneva] will be frustrated.*
> *The days will become weeks,*
> *Then months, then years, and fail.*
> *Lawmakers condemned by their powerlessness.*

Nostradamus made other predictions regarding WWII, including the technical advances that allowed its mass destructiveness. For example, he predicted the invention of airplanes, air battles (Quatrain IV-43), and bombs (Quatrain V-8). In Quatrain III-13, he described submarines: "When the submerged military swims underwater." He referred to the periscope as "the eye of the sea" (Quatrain IV-15) and spoke of war by means of "iron fish" (submariners still refer to torpedoes as fish). He may even have described Polaris/Trident missile submarines when he wrote "fish that travels over land and sea…from the sea it reaches the enemy's walls" (Quatrain I-29). Elsewhere he defined those missiles as a "mechanism of flying fire" (Quatrain III-34). He predicted WWII would end with a new weapon: "Fire the color of gold from Heaven to Earth will be seen…great murder of mankind…" (Quatrain II-92). How much more accurately could a person living 400 years ago describe such developments?

On a happier note, Nostradamus also made predictions that applaud mankind. For example, he wrote of the year man would first fly in the air with balloons and actually named Montgolfier as the inventor (Quatrain V-59). He predicted the invention of iron ships (Quatrain II-5), safe air travel (Quatrain I-63), and the rocket ship (Quatrain II-46), claiming that a large rocket would carry man to "Luna" [the moon] (Quatrain IX-65).

Nostradamus also spoke of more recent political events. For example, he wrote about the Shah of Iran, saying that the King of Persia (the former name of Iran) would be dethroned after many powerful years by a religious coup started in Paris (Quatrain I-70). The Ayatollah Khomeini did launch a religious campaign against the Shah and did start the rebellion while he was still in Paris.

Referring to America, Nostradamus spoke of three great brothers. Many scholars maintain that this can only pertain to the Kennedys. They point to Quatrain I-26, which stated that a great man will suddenly be assassinated in the middle of the day, and the other will fall in the middle of the night. Of course, President John Kennedy was fatally wounded on the afternoon of November 22, 1963, and his brother, Senator Robert Kennedy, died very late at night after winning the California Presidential Primary on June 5, 1968. Nostradamus may have provided a second warning in Quatrain X-26: "The successor will revenge his beautiful [handsome] brother…his death will abuse his blood." Did Nostradamus have anything to say about the fate of the third brother, Edward Kennedy? It seems that he attempted to leave a strong warning: "In the year of war a Pope named Paul and the third brother will be killed" (Quatrain VIII-46). War is a common warning by Nostradamus.

The present Pope is named Paul, and he has already survived one assassination attempt. Whether John Paul II is the Pope to whom Nostradamus was referring is not clear. However, Nostradamus gave a better clue as to who will be behind the plots and the year that his next attempt may come: "The Antichrist shall [separately] annihilate three good [men]...27 bloodletting years his war [against them] will last" (Quatrain VIII-77). The first brother was murdered in 1963. If the war (struggle) is to last 27 years, then according to Nostradamus 1990 may be a treacherous time for the Kennedys, the papacy, and the world. Nostradamus may have gone further and predicted when in 1991[*] this may occur: "Not far from Easter...the third brother wounded and murdered" (Quatrain IX-36). No sane person wants these predictions to come true. Yet, the only way to avoid them may be by paying close attention and taking preventive action.

Nostradamus also made many predictions for events still in our future, many of which now seem plausible knowing today's technology. Many are still cloaked in mystery, but one thing is certain: The future events that Nostradamus wrote about are very disconcerting.

Nostradamus clearly described a third World War and the man behind the resulting worldwide destruction—the third Antichrist. Some scholars of Nostradamus claim that the third Antichrist will be an almost inhuman destroyer of life who will use deception to unite the Islamic peoples of the world. It is not difficult to recognize that the Arabs are presently in a unique position. The Arab states are strategically positioned around Israel, and they have the political power (through control of oil), the human resources (hundreds of millions of devout followers), considerable financial strength (U.S. dollars), and the military hardware (Russian support) to start WWIII. This war is predicted to start between the early to mid-1990s.

---

[*]Since a new year begins between November (when John Kennedy was assassinated) and Easter (when Edward Kennedy is predicted to die), the season correlating with the prediction is spring 1991, the time when the primaries will start for the 1992 Presidential election.

In Quatrain VIII-100, Nostradamus described the escalating cold war as a time when great military spending will create economic woe, but he stated further that these woes will be minor compared with the use of that military capability. The use and effects of that military strength are described in Quatrain II-5, which warns of submarines used to cross the Mediterranean Sea in a war with Italy. This attack, according to Quatrain IX-69, will result in destruction of two-thirds of the Italian population. Did Nostradamus give a clue about who will start this great war? Yes, in Quatrain V-25:

> *The Arabian prince, Mars, the sun, and Venus [in] Leo.*
> *The reign of the church will be overcome by the sea,*
> *On the side of the Persians [Iran] with an advantage of*
>   *nearly a million,*
> *Byzantium [Turkey] and Egypt are the secret origins of*
>   *the invasion.*

Persia and Byzantium are the ancient names of Iran and Turkey, respectively. Egypt, Iran, and Turkey (with other nations of the Middle East) were all once united in the Ottoman Empire, and they are still committed to their common religion—Islam.

Although the predicted conflict will start with the use of conventional weapons, Nostradamus predicted (as well as anyone could in the sixteenth century) that the Third World War will eventually involve nuclear weapons (Quatrain II-92). "Fire the color of gold from the Earth to the sky...great murder of mankind." In Quatrain I-22, he may have alluded to the effects of nuclear winter, stating that many would be lost (killed) by the cold and ice. He also predicted that the first destruction of cities by nuclear weapons since Hiroshima and Nagasaki (Quatrain II-6) will occur in July 1999 (Quatrain X-72). Nuclear war before the turn of the century was also described in Quatrains I-16 and II-46. Indeed, Nostradamus listed so much death and destruction that it seems many cities and governments will no longer exist and that almost nowhere on Earth will law and decency survive.

Nostradamus also predicted some of the conditions that will help bring about WWIII. He predicted fire, flood, and famine, the likes of which the world has never seen, for the first time to be experienced worldwide: "When the great comet [as yet undiscovered] makes its run (Quatrain II-62)...rivers and lakes will boil hectic" (Quatrains V-98 and II-3). Worldwide drought will last for many years, eventually engulfing the whole world (Quatrain I-17). So scarce will water and food be that "man will become eaters of men" (Quatrain II-75).

Nostradamus also wrote about other contributing factors that will cause world upset and world war. For example, he stated that monetary values will collapse, great inflation will occur, (Quatrain VII-28) and financial credit will be a major problem because the world will become blinded by lust (materialism). These statements became more meaningful after the introduction of paper money, which did not exist during Nostradamus' time. According to Nostradamus, all these events must occur several years before 1994 if they are to influence the outbreak of war.

Nostradamus wrote of one more major catastrophe that will create havoc and destruction worldwide—earthquakes. He wrote of a particularly severe earthquake that is to occur in the month of May (Quatrains X-67 and IX-83). Many feel that this is the same great quake that will send fire from the center of the Earth to destroy the new (American) city (Quatrain I-87). By combining other quatrains, some scholars have concluded that this earthquake will be so massive as to destroy buildings worldwide, "leaving no place on Earth to grab a firm foothold."

That is quite a message. Certainly, the parts about WWIII agree with Washington's prophecies. Nostradamus' mention of world upheaval also has something in common with the Apostle John, who wrote the Book of Revelation.

JOHN

John was the most beloved disciple of Christ. He was the last of the disciples to remain alive and was the last to write his gospel. John also wrote the last book in the Bible, entitled the

Apocalypse, or the Book of Revelation. This scripture received the latter title because it is the only book in the New Testament that is dedicated to revealing the future. Written 1,893 years ago, the book deals exclusively with our future, known as "the endtime," and aids in clarifying the Old Testament prophesies of Daniel, Ezekiel, and Isaias.

The Old Testament often refers to this endtime as a period "when man becomes very knowledgeable" and when "people travel great distances very quickly."* The New Testament also refers to this period as the time "when you will hear of wars and rumors of wars...nation will rise against nation, and kingdom against kingdom; and there will be earthquakes in various places and pestilences and famines" (Mark 13:7, 8 and Matt. 24:6–8). "When you see these things coming to pass know that it is near..." (Mark 13:29 and Matt. 24:13).

Certainly, in today's computerized, high technology world, man has greatly increased his scientific accomplishments. Only since the turn of the century has man brought internal plumbing to the home, developed microbiology, produced artificial organs, and rearranged DNA. The last 85 years have seen the birth of electronics, the invention of the airplane, the introduction of plastics, the development of worldwide communications, nuclear energy, space travel, and the minicomputer. This can be expressed graphically. If man's accumulated knowledge of the 6,000 years previous to 1940 was represented by a stone one inch in height, then man's knowledge in 1986 would be represented by the Washington Monument which is 6,665 inches tall. Man has indeed become knowledgeable in recent times.

For almost 2,000 years after John wrote the Book of Revelation, man traveled by horse. Traveling a great distance quickly meant riding at 10 mph without stopping overnight for sleep. Even as recently as 1910 when the first coast to coast automobile trip was made, travel was slow. The trip took 71 days

---

*This is paraphrased from many sections of the Old Testament, including Isaias 44:25 and 5:26–29.

with an average speed of just 4 mph. Presently, of course, people travel at 60 mph every day in hundreds of millions of automobiles, and thousands of people a day traverse the globe in hours by 600 mph jets. Even higher speeds are achieved by astronauts and intercontinental missiles which transit continents at 15,000 mph—speeds that were truly uncomprehensible just a few years ago.

The world at present could not be described as at peace. Globally there are about 25 wars,* though none of these conflicts at the moment are global. But how many people today are unconcerned about Arab-Israeli threats that may trigger world conflict? Iran and Iraq maintain that since they are no longer at war with each other they will go to war with Israel. Israel threatens to invade Lebanon because of guerillas positioned in strongholds at its border. Syria threatens to invade Israel if the Golan Heights are not returned. Elsewhere in the world, African nations are at war with neighboring countries, Pakistan is threatening India, China has border disputes with Vietnam, and Latin American nations are engaged in major fighting. American war planes shoot down Libyan fighters and support retaliatory attacks against its capitol. Central American nations claim the United States is preparing to invade, as fighting continues in Nicaragua, El Salvador and Costa Rica. Although recent trends are again toward détente, Russian and American land and sea-based nuclear weapons are still poised to destroy each other "and most of the world" at a moment's notice. How could this period be more accurately described than as "a time of wars and rumors of wars?"

In the Book of Revelation, John said the world would lose most of its population through a combination of unnatural causes and the actions of the "Antichrist." For example, in Rev. 9:3–5 John described a great plague that will affect everyone like the sting of a scorpion for five months. A scorpion cannot kill

---

*Presently wars are being fought in the following countries: Angola, Namibia, Chad, Ethiopia, Western Sahara, Mozambique, South Africa, Sudan, Uganda, Burma, India, Indonesia, Kampuchea, Laos, Vietnam, Philippines, Sri Lanka, Colombia, El Salvador, Guatemala, Nicaragua, Peru, and Lebanon. Not considered as wars are conflicts such as those in Israel and Northern Ireland.

people, but it has the most painful venom known. He also talked about new diseases, not unlike AIDS, that will cause people's bodies to be covered in sores and will make them wish they were dead (Rev. 16:2). John described an earthquake, the likes of which the world has never seen, that will destroy the world's cities and lay waste every island in the sea (Rev. 16:18–20).

John went on to explain that as a result of unnatural events and war, a third of the Earth (and its population) will be destroyed, a third of the Earth's trees and grasses will be burned, one-third of all ships and sea life will be eliminated, and one-third of all the Earth's rivers, lakes, and fountains (springs) will be poisoned (Rev. 2:7–11). The rest of the world is not to escape unharmed, for John prophesied worldwide drought, with the sun (or atmospheric conditions) changed to scorch mankind and to dry up rivers (Rev. 16:8–12). Such a drought would totally disrupt the world's food production and have profound effects on the world's economy as well as its political and military stability. Under such circumstances, man's pride and nationalism would be nonexistent as he desperately struggled for daily survival.

SUPPORTING PROPHESIES

The Book of Revelation describes a seven-year tribulation, during which the Antichrist will take over the world and torture and kill all who will not worship him as God. This is the same Antichrist that Nostradamus described by position and function. The Book of Revelation also mentions the great war of the endtime. This Third World War as described by John will dwarf all the wars before it as enormous armies are committed to battle. One nation alone is to deploy an army of 200-million soldiers (Rev. 9:15, 16). In John's time, the known population of the world had not reached 200-million people. Today, China has the world's largest army, and it coincidentally boasts that it can muster an army of 200 million.

Other prophecies of the New Testament concur with the magnitude of the expected devastation, stating that "unless these days be shortened no flesh could survive" (Mark 13:20 and Matt. 24:22).

As great and final as the climactic battle of WWIII may be, prophecy indicates that it will not start on a worldwide scale but, rather, gradually encompass the whole world. As shown earlier, Washington envisioned WWIII and the subsequent burning of American cities. It is clear that Nostradamus foresaw the same destiny (Quatrain II-19):

> *Newcomers shall build a place without defenses,*
> *...In a place that was not inhabited,*
> *Meadows, houses, and towns will be had at pleasure.*
> *Extensive arable land will have famine, plague, and war.*

Nostradamus seems to be describing America: a new place built by a new people, a place of pleasure without walls and with extensive arable land. Nostradamus is consistent in calling America the "new" land and its cities "new" cities. This is reasonable because when this quatrain was written, America only recently had been discovered, and was mostly uninhabited. Yet, Nostradamus' description of the "land of pleasure" also applies to modern America, as the United States leads the world in "leisure time" and recreational expenditures.

Isolated by two oceans, America is truly without walls. As many immigrants have found, much of the Canadian and Mexican borders are not even demarcated by a line of paint between the countries. As for agricultural land, what other nation has the United States' reputation for abundance? If indeed this quatrain pertains to the United States, then the last line seems to state the destiny of America.

As shown earlier, Nostradamus predicted that the war would become nuclear by 1999. In Quatrain II-91, he accurately described the flash, suction, and fireball that accompany a nuclear explosion. Furthermore, he stated the time of day when this terrible deed will be enacted;

At sunrise a great fire the people will see,
Noise and light in the direction of a strong wind,
Within the circle of death, screams we will hear,
Through acts of war–fire, famine–alas until death.

If the war is to begin on a small scale, what will be the starting point or the first target? Nostradamus answered this question in Quatrain X-49:

Garden of the world near the new city,
Among the roads of the carved out mountains,
[It shall be] struck and plunged into the vat,
Forced to drink poisonous sulphur waters.

According to Nostradamus, the nuclear strike will not be against military targets, industrial complexes, or oil fields, but rather, a major modern city with skyscrapers. It would appear that the areas surrounding this hub of the world will not escape the effects of poisonous fallout. What city is he referring to by the term "new city?" The answer may be in Quatrain VI-97:

[At] 5 and 40 degrees, from burning heavens
Fire comes to the great new city,
Instant great flames fiercely fly.

Experts agree that this quatrain can refer only to New York.

Although Washington did not name any specific city in his prophecy, John did. Of the first great city to be destroyed during the endtime, John wrote (Rev. 18:16-18): "'Woe, woe, the great city, which was clothed in fine linen and purple and scarlet, and precious stone, and pearls; for in one hour riches so great were laid waste!' and every shipmaster, and everyone who sails to a place, and mariners, and all who work upon the sea stood afar off, and cried out as they saw the place of her burning, saying 'what city is like to this great city?'" And in Rev. 18:21: "with this violence will Babylon, the great city, be overthrown, and will not be found any more."

Why compare New York to the wicked city of Babylon?* Perhaps because it is the center of child pornography, lurid sex, violence, corruption, drugs, and organized crime, as well as trade and finance.

The articles of history presented here substantiate the validity of prophets. Their usefulness to history, both past and future, is difficult to ignore. Particularly significant is the definite correlation among the prophesies of Washington, Nostradamus, and John. What they predicted many centuries ago has come true with amazing accuracy. This suggests that their predictions for the future will also come true. If so, it seems that mankind should, in the near future, prepare for some worldwide upheavals, the likes of which may be hard to imagine. These prophecies suggest that the Earth and our social structure are unstable and capable of great and sudden change.

The next chapters examine the causes and consequences of worldwide instabilities and compares those findings with the most current scientific knowledge. This investigation and its results are based not upon imagination but, rather, upon science and the prophetic works of Washington, Nostradamus, and John.

---

*The ancient city of Babylon was the largest and most splendid (and by some accounts the most lustful) city in the world during the first millennium B.C. and is presently being renovated. Coincidentally, the only city in the world (other than the ancient ruins in Iraq) named Babylon is located just 25 miles east of New York City.

III. FINANCIAL INSTABILITY:
Motives, Debt, and Automation

For almost 2,000 years, theologians have tried to anticipate the coming of the prophesied tribulation period and the return of the Messiah by deciphering the meaning of 666—the mark of the satanic endtime beast.

In the Book of Revelation, sometimes called the Apocalypse, the Apostle John wrote about the seven-year endtime tribulation, the Second Coming, and 666. The number 666 is thought of as the symbol of the third Antichrist, the person who is going to control the world and cause many wars, including the next world war. John warned that the Antichrist would dominate the world during the tribulation—the last seven years before Christ returned to Earth. He stated: "It [the beast] will cause all...to have a mark on their right hand or on their foreheads...no one may be able to buy or sell, except him who has the mark...and its number is six hundred and sixty-six" (Rev. 13:16–18). And he said: "If anyone...receives a mark upon his forehead or upon his hand...he shall be tormented with fire...their torment goes up [on] forever and ever; and they rest neither day nor night…anyone who receives the mark..." (Rev. 14:9). Pretty strong words. According to John, mankind can be forgiven for many things, but not for taking the mark of the beast.

RAPTURE

How God could be so loving yet so stern has troubled many people. Any explanation of this ambivalence cannot be scientific. It is a matter of faith that mankind should behave according to the rules of the Bible and that those who do not are unworthy of reward and will be punished.

Biblical scholars debate something called the rapture, which is the sudden removal of the devout followers of Christ from the Earth. Some scholars believe in the rapture, and others do not. Also, when the rapture is to occur is debatable. But hopefully, if it is to occur, it will before the Antichrist takes over the world.

One thought is that the Church is what is preventing the emergence of the Antichrist. If this is true, then would the rapture of the Church start the seven-year tribulation? In the New Testament, Christ said: ..."Upon this rock I will build my Church and the gates of hell shall not prevail against it" (Matt. 16:18). This would signify that Satan cannot run completely rampant on the Earth—he cannot have total control. If Satan is restrained by God, then perhaps the Antichrist's coming is being restrained by the presence of God's Church. Even though there are different denominations, Christian churches may be providing the "cork" that contains the Antichrist.

What then would restrain the Antichrist if the Church and all its true members were suddenly removed? True Church followers, regardless of denomination, are not as numerous as Christians might like to believe. The devout members of the Church are not just people who show up on Sundays, but true, practicing believers in God and His law. If these devout followers are instantly transformed and brought to meet the Lord via the rapture, then they will avoid the terrible tribulation. With the Church removed, the Antichrist may be allowed to come to power as the Book of Revelation graphically describes.

Surely, understanding the mark or the symbol of 666 is paramount to recognizing the satanic beast. Obviously, anyone with a large 666 stamped across his forehead would be immediately recognized and opposed, as would anyone who advocated such markings. Yet, John clearly attempted to give us a definite sign so we will recognize the beast. The rest of this chapter attempts to reveal the identity of the beast. Instead of following the common lines of a lecture or argument, an unbiased, factual approach is taken. It begins with a departure from the Biblical approaches to examine motives.

MOTIVES

Sometimes understanding a complex subject requires delving into seemingly unrelated background information, which later becomes clearly relevant. In this section, such a path is followed. References to some publicly known families are made but no malice is intended, and no wrongdoing is implied. The recurrence of certain names demonstrates a basic commonality of the items discussed that is important to the central theme of this chapter. This interdependence becomes evident as the chapter unfolds. Total acceptance of all independent parts of this theme is not required to substantiate the conclusion as a likely possibility.

The Pacific Electric

In 1920 an advanced prototype mass transit system ran regularly and inexpensively in Los Angeles, California. Like many early rail systems, the Pacific Electric was corporately owned and operated. This pilot line demonstrated how cities profitably and efficiently could provide mass transit. The line carried 200-million passengers annually and was heralded throughout the country as a great breakthrough in technology and a major advancement for society. This rail system not only provided inexpensive, comfortable transportation, but also stimulated urban growth by extending its tracks beyond the city boundaries. It was this easy access within the city and between its center and suburbia that helped Los Angeles become the largest city in America and encouraged its phenomenal growth from 5,000 people to 2.5 million in only 70 years. The "Big Red" rail cars of the Pacific Electric were also the only electric cars that were standard gauge (4' 8") instead of narrow gauge (3' 6"). This allowed the 1,200 miles of track to be used as a standard freight car line as well as a rapid transit line, thus multiplying its profits further.

However, after receiving all of this acclaim, the Pacific Electric suddenly ceased to exist. It literally disappeared. Why? The reason was that the rights-of-way were sold, the bridges were disassembled for scrap, the track was removed, and the rolling stock was exported to Mexico, Argentina, Brazil, and other countries in Latin America. Why would the owners have done that? The original owners would not have. The second owners were interested in profit, but not from their mass transit company. They also had substantial interests in the Southern Pacific Railroad, which was being threatened by a loss in commuter service and, even worse, it was losing valuable freight haulage. The "need to do something" became uncontainable.

After receiving national acclaim for his successes in Los Angeles, Henry Huntington, founder and chairman of Pacific Electric, announced plans for mass transit in other coastal California cities and was planning an interstate electric railroad to connect them to the East. Henry Harrison, president of Southern Pacific, became anxious not to see his Southern California losses extend to other parts of the nation. He therefore pushed for laws to lower intracity transit to 3 cents for an all-day fare to guarantee major losses for the rival railroad, the Pacific Electric.[5] When this failed, he bid against Pacific Electric for new line licenses, paying 10 times their maximum value to prevent the Pacific Electric's continued growth. Finally, Southern Pacific Railroad bought 45 percent of Pacific Electric stock, forcing the remaining stockholders to sell their interests.

After gaining full control, Southern Pacific caused Pacific Electric to cut back service and to sell many rights-of-way. This not only reduced its capacity and convenience, but also caused the trains to run down crowded streets, greatly hampering the speed and safety of the system. Southern Pacific also allowed multiple grade crossings, further slowing car speeds to an average of 13 mph. Some of Southern Pacific's longest corridors were paved into freeways. The result was that the Pacific Electric mass transit system was no longer the American model. Columns were placed through the Hollywood subway to support freeway overpasses, and the subway was sealed shut. Buses replaced electric cars, Pacific Electric went out of business, and the Southern Pacific Railroad regained its customers and freight haulage.

Ironically, big cities such as New York and Chicago have expensive, if not efficient, mass transit rail systems, but America's largest and most populated city, which once had the best, now has none.

Connections

Although cloaked in secrecy, the source of the money used to buy out the Pacific Electric is believed to have been the auto and oil industries. These industries shared Southern Pacific's strong interest in defeating efficient mass transit. According to a federal court case, the giant oil conglomerate, Standard Oil, played a major role.

Originally founded under a different name in 1865 by John D. Rockefeller, the fledgling Standard Oil Company grew to be the largest corporation in the world—not because Rockefeller knew the most about oil, but because he knew best how to manipulate people.

One of the first daring moves that Rockefeller made was to ship his oil by rail. To obtain the reduced rates needed to be competitive, he had to guarantee the railroads far more oil shipments than any producer could possibly supply. The deal provided that a kickback be paid to Rockefeller for each barrel of oil shipped, regardless of who did the shipping. Since kickbacks are illegal, a new word was coined—the rebate. As Standard Oil took advantage of the lower rates, the other oil companies had to switch from shipping by wagon to transport by rail to stay competitive. However, no oil freight rate was as low as Rockefeller's because of his unique kickback.[6]

As the oil industry started to boom, the cash-poor railroads began paying Rockefeller in stock and, thus, he was able to make a bid for control of them. However, once he gained control of the rail lines, he refused to ship oil for companies he targeted for buy out. An oil company that could not ship its product competitively would not be profitable and, therefore, its value would drop. Rockefeller then would buy the manipulated company at a fraction of its former value.

As Standard Oil became dominant, Rockefeller threatened to cut off all business with anyone dealing with other oil companies.

This illegal practice drove out the remainder of his competition, with many individuals being financially ruined. No one was spared as even his own brother Frank was wiped out, creating a wound in the family that was never healed.

Rockefeller expanded Standard Oil nationally, getting around federal and state law by using his power (bribery) to pass legislation allowing formation of a new type of company, the "trust." Never before were companies chartered to control companies. This gave Rockefeller the freedom to expand Standard Oil without interference from the individual states.

To guarantee total control of the oil industry, Rockefeller used his growing power in new and dynamic ways. For example, he gave shares of stock in Standard Oil to bank executives for their "cooperation" in withdrawing credit from competitors. Rockefeller authorized the sale of oil products to the customers of targeted competitors below cost to force the competition into bankruptcy. He then increased prices to compensate for lost profits. In some cases, Standard Oil was accused of bribing competitors' accountants to spy and/or doctor their books to Rockefeller's advantage.

One of the most remarkable instances concerned a ship company that was to build the first long oil pipeline. Rockefeller considered a pipeline a direct threat to his railroad oil shipping monopoly. He bought up rights-of-way to block the pipeline, started labor unrest, and intimidated workers and equipment suppliers. He also had the pipeline sabotaged, and bribed key people in high positions to create stockholder distrust and discontentment. The result? Standard Oil bought out its would-be competitor, Tidewater, and, capitalizing on the Tidewater concepts, built major pipelines of its own.[6]

Within 15 years of entering the competitive oil industry, the Standard Oil Company controlled 95 percent of all oil production in America and many other businesses. With such a history of buying out or destroying the competition, it is not difficult to understand why the unproven connection between the Pacific

Electric, the Southern Pacific,* and John D. Rockefeller's Standard Oil persists.†

Watergate

As seemingly unrelated as it may appear, Watergate can demonstrate a central point.‡ Watergate centered on a paranoid person who was deathly afraid that he was going to lose an election. President Richard Nixon was at different times associated with large sums of money in suitcases moving around the countryside. A fellow member of his political party, though not a supporter of his, was Nelson Rockefeller. Rockefeller was Governor of the State of New York for many years and had attempted to become the Republican candidate for the Presidency three separate times. Rockefeller lost the nomination in 1964 to Barry Goldwater and twice, in 1960 and 1968, to Nixon. In his last bid for the nomination, Rockefeller spent over $8 million. After so many attempts, the aging Rocky recognized that he was never going to win the nomination, let alone the election, using the same strategy.

You may remember that Rockefeller made campaign loans to Nixon during his 1972 campaign. Politics can indeed make strange bedfellows. President Nixon needed large sums of cash, but it should be obvious that Rockefeller wanted something as well.

---

*Standard Oil (of California) also owned the Northern Pacific Railroad, which merged with the Southern Pacific in 1930.

†A federal jury concluded (upheld on appeal) that Standard Oil (of California), General Motors and Firestone Tire, were guilty of influencing (bribing) city officials, and of conspiracy to destroy public mass transit in 45 U.S. cities. Although the federal prosecutor demanded prison sentences for corporate officers the judge elected to impose a fine of one dollar each.[7]

‡Sometimes examining all the possibilities means putting on a detective's hat and speculating to see how the pieces may fit together and what the big picture may be. (This is especially true if information is suppressed or falsified.) The next couple of paragraphs are unlike the rest of this book in that they are suppositions and cannot be proved. If you do not agree with the interpretation made, so be it, but do not "throw out the baby with the bath water" and feel that everything else presented can be discounted as well.

Speculate for a moment that Rockefeller wanted to be appointed Vice President of the United States, should that office become available. Nixon would have seen no particular problem with that objective. But Rocky could guarantee that Agnew would vacate that office by exposing the Vice President's involvement with building contractors and the like, with whom Agnew had a long and sordid history. Agnew's activities were fairly obvious to many people in government who were willing to look the other way for lack of interest.

You may also recall that the Secretary of State under Richard Nixon was Henry Kissinger (September 1973 through January 1977). If he were American born, Kissinger would have been fourth in line for the Presidency in the event of Nixon's death or removal from office. The Secretary of State has a powerful position. He has access to what is going on inside the White House, the Pentagon, and Washington in general. An amazing coincidence is that for 18 years before becoming Secretary of State for Nixon, Kissinger (who also taught at Harvard) was Special Studies Director and Foreign Affairs Advisor for the Rockefeller Foundation. This foundation, controlled by the Rockefellers and their heirs, has strong influence in many countries worldwide and has at times been accused of being politically involved in foreign governments.[*] Kissinger not only was hand picked by Rockefeller, but was one of his strongest supporters. The deep feelings of Kissinger may best be exemplified by the following excerpts:[8]

> ...Kissinger fought against Nixon's nomination. He told radio host Casper Citron that "Rockefeller is the only candidate...with a program to focus America on its purposes." And that he had "grave doubts that Nixon can bridge the gap..."

---

[*] It is perhaps not uncommon for large, powerful, capitalistic groups or organizations to be accused of political coups or covert activities. No attempt here is intended to substantiate or disprove such claims.

Kissinger has denied the vehemence that some reporters have attributed to him, when he spoke in terms of Nixon as being at best "average in politics and below average in thinking."

[President Elect] Nixon sent for Kissinger and had his secret meeting at the Hotel Pierre in New York, after which Kissinger was offered the title of Assistant to the President for national security affairs.... Kissinger discussed his offer from Nixon with Rockefeller in three separate meetings. Rockefeller was not displeased...he would have a good contact inside the White House,...

After the above appointment, a wire service reporter asked Kissinger for an evaluation of his future boss.... "Ridiculous," Kissinger said...when asked for his opinion of Nixon as President, "Even more ridiculous," Kissinger added.

So Nixon asked a political enemy, a former German-Jewish brush salesman to be Secretary of State. Henry (Heinz) maintained close contact with Nelson Rockefeller and became the second most powerful figure in the U.S. Government. The Vice President's office became vacant (twice), and Rockefeller was appointed to fill the vacancy.

The fact that there was more to Rockefeller than he would let on was demonstrated by his reply to the Senate during his appointment ratification hearing. When Rockefeller was asked what his net worth was, he answered that he "did not know exactly but thought it to be about $8 million." About $108 million was closer to a believable amount according to one senator. The extent of the Rockefeller wealth was revealed in part by the public offering of a portion of Rockefeller Center (one of many holdings), which on the first day of the stock's issue was worth $1,000 million.[*]

Nixon was forced out of the White House by the Watergate scandal, which was exposed by the investigative reporting of the *Washington Post*. The *Post* reporters freely admitted that they did not know what was going on. They continued in their pursuit only because they kept receiving information from "Deep Throat," the unknown, quiet person who stayed in the background and told the reporters where to look for clues. Apparently, there was an effort to make it appear that the information was "uncovered" from the outside to prevent suspicion of an inside source.

Although evidence is lacking, is it possible that a powerful, ambitious, enterprising opportunist, such as Nelson Rockefeller, with designs on the Presidency, could have arranged to be made Vice President knowing that it was easy to get rid of Agnew? Could such a person with direct connections to high positions in the White House arrange to leak the information necessary for the *Washington Post* to uncover Nixon's Watergate activities so that the President would be impeached or forced to resign? That simple plan could have made Rocky President of the United States without having won a presidential election or even a nomination.

Is that plot inconceivable when his key man in international affairs happened to be Secretary of State under Nixon anyway? Suppose Nixon, through all his turmoil, began to suspect this plot. Could Nixon have preferred to name someone as his successor that he could trust, such as Ford? Could Nixon have prearranged his pardon by Ford for criminal actions in return for the appointment? Could he also have arranged to fulfill his promise to have Rockefeller appointed as Vice President after the Presidency was already filled? Is that too much wheeling and dealing to expect from American politicians?

---

[*]In August 1985, 71.5 percent of Rockefeller Center was offered to the public for $1.3 billion, of which $0.4 billion was to be used to buy the land under the center. The proceeds permitted Rockefeller heirs to convert their holdings into cash. The total worth of the property after the $0.4 billion was reinvested was $2.2 billion, of which 28.5 percent is still controlled by the original shareholders.

Financial Power

In the late 1700s, Mayer Amschel Bauer opened a small shop in Frankfurt. Over the door he hung a red shield. As a result, he became known as Red Shield or, in German, "Rothschild."

Mayer realized that to maximize profits in financial matters, one had to deal in large amounts of money and that countries and kings were among those most in need of large sums of capital. Mayer lent money to kings of Europe that he had borrowed from other kings who had a surplus. The lending kings wished to avoid the politics of international loans. Not only did Mayer receive a handsome profit for handling the transactions, but he also received the kings' debts of gratitude. But Mayer was no fool; he knew that a king could be removed or decide not to pay back the loan. So, as a condition of the loan, he insisted on being put in control of the money and banking of the nation. Thus, the Central Bank was founded. The power he foresaw in financial control is exemplified by his statement: "Give me control over a nation's currency and I care not who makes its laws."[14]

Today, it is well recognized that the shape and destiny of Europe were affected greatly by the power and wealth of the Rothschild family and their financial and banking institutions. The Rothschilds started commercial banking in 1804 and gave international banking a new meaning while quickly gaining enormous assets and financial wealth. Soon they had family members heading up banks in all the major European nations. With so much financial power under central dominance, they were able to control economies, trade, and military spending.

Rothschild exerted financial control over European stock markets as well. His ability to deceive the working class for tremendous gain was made obvious during the Battle of Waterloo in 1815. It was well known that Napoleon was about to meet the Duke of Wellington on the battlefields of Belgium. What was not known was the outcome of the battle. If Wellington won, the nervous market would have a strong rally. If Napoleon won, the fear of a long war and invasion would drive the market to all-time lows.

Because timely information is of utmost importance to people in control, Rothschild had set up an elaborate courier network to deliver international news and messages. Thus, everyone knew that the Rothschild messenger would sail into the harbor bringing the first news of the battle's outcome. Everyone also knew that Rothschild was waiting at the pier to meet the courier personally so that he could be the first to act upon the news.

However, before the ship reached port, it sent coded flag signals to Rothschild, who then rushed to the stock market and sold everything he owned. Prices immediately began to plummet as more investors sold based upon Rothschild's inside information. By the middle of the afternoon, when Rothschild left the stock market, stock values were a tiny fraction of the morning's opening. What was not known was that Rothschild secretly had arranged for close associates to buy up all the depressed stock at the close of the day. The following day when the defeat of Napoleon became known, the stock market rallied and Rothschild realized a 10-fold profit in one day. Such activities are now illegal, but laws to prevent such abuse are written only after many people have been abused.

The recognition of such families may have prompted some to believe that cooperation between influential groups would create a powerful force over their future.

If the richest and most powerful people of the world were united they could use their political and economic influence to sway governments and economies and thus control the course of the world. It is believed that they could accomplish a great many things for their own betterment and eventual world domination only at the expense of the freedom and well-being of the masses.

According to lectures by Dr. John Coleman entitled The Club Of Rome,* the success of private associations to destabilize governments and create revolutions for their personal betterment dates back to the French Revolution and are even more powerful today.

---

*Dr. John Coleman goes on to give exact details of present ambitions and activities. He also names many government officials and prominent family names that are not within the scope of this presentation.

Dr. Coleman names famous people and institutions (this publication chooses not to reprint these) that have been linked to worldwide destabilization. He points out that financial backing from groups in America and Europe put a devout Christian nation in its death throes by allowing the Bolshevik Revolution to succeed and thus establish Communism in Russia, which at the time under Alexander Kerensky was a Democratic Republic.* Why, you may ask, would anyone want to belong to such an organization?

Let us go one step further. Are you aware that U.S. banks and Western banks have loaned Russia and its satellites hundreds of billions of dollars? Our national debt is $2.35 trillion, and most of it was spent trying to build up more military capability (ours and that of our allies) to offset the growth of the militaristic arm of Russia.†

As every child in school is taught, banks are essential. Banks take money from someone who does not need it in the short term and let others use the value of that money to build a house or a business. This system of loans generates more money and wealth for the borrower and the country as a whole. Therefore, lending money to someone is giving him a helping hand. The government, for instance, does not lend money for the benefit of interest, but rather to help those in need and to stimulate growth and the economy. The whole American economy is based on government

---

*The two largest financial powers on Wall Street—the Morgans and Rockefellers—reportedly contributed hundreds of millions of dollars to support Lenin and the Bolshevik Revolution (Russian Communist Party). The man who headed the fund raising for the Russian Communists was Paul Warburg, a member of the Board of Governors of the Federal Reserve. Warburg, the first person to have this title, held this position through most of WWI at the same time that the German immigrant's brother, Max, was the Head of the Bank of Germany (the German Central Bank).[14] The fact that two banking brothers headed the funding of both sides of the first world war is too significant to be coincidental.

†In a strange twist of circumstances, the British settled a 70-year-old debt in 1986 and collected $60 million. The Russians finally agreed to the $0.06 billion payment only after the British Government agreed to "forgive" the $69 billion balance of the loan. The amount received was less then 1/10 of a penny on the dollar. Now that this dispute is settled, Russia's credit for more loans has improved.

loans and subsidies. Since the primary purpose is not to earn interest, money is loaned to countries throughout the world at less than the prime rate.

In a sense, when you put money in the bank, you put work in the bank. Consider Americans working 40 hours a week building railroads, bridges, and ships, scraping to put some savings away in the bank. Taking that labor, which is represented by money, and shipping it to some other country is like shipping that country work. The process is not instantaneous because it takes time to build a railroad with the money lent them, but in effect the other country was shipped a railroad.

Realize that the United States is not allowed to send Russia precision ball bearings (except under Nixon, who allowed Russia to use them in its guidance systems so that its missiles could be more accurate). We certainly do not want Russia building pipelines so that it can make money selling oil to the Europeans and thereby build up its armaments. No, but we have given Russia hundreds of billions of dollars. Instead of selling oil, all the Russians have to do is take out loans. Who would lend money to the Russians? Bankers and businessmen who want to make money. Especially now, with "nice guy" Gorbachev in power, U.S. and other banks and businesses are more willing than ever to lend Russia money or to develop enterprises to strengthen its failing economy.

Singer, Monsanto, Eli Lilli, Occidental Petroleum, and Combustion Engineering are among 100 American corporations considering Russian expansion.[9] England, West Germany, France, Italy, and Japan extended billions of dollars of credit in 1988 alone.

Congressman Jack Kemp (R-NY) said "...there is every indication that the Soviet Union is preparing to enter the Eurobond Market, ...thereby tapping American pension funds [as a lending source]..."[10]

Lenders will never see their money again. Like many Third World nations, Russia currently borrows more each month in new loans than is due on existing loans. Because Russia is a closed society, its assets are secret and its business transactions confidential. Thus, Russian loans are essentially unsecured. The same gold and oil probably have been used as collateral to several nations simultaneously,* and government operated industries would never be "given over" to foreign banks in case of default.

The world banking system has been dominated by five major banks in America: CitiCorp, Chase Manhattan, Irving Trust, Chemical Bank, and Bank of America. It has been and still is considered good business to lend money to the Russians. In addition, if Russia built up its army or a navy or an air force, America would have to increase its military strength as well. How would America finance such a buildup? It would borrow from the banks! What a lovely system! The banks lend money to both sides. By encouraging decades of a cold war arms race, the banks have supported potential global destruction.

Who was the chairman of the board of Chase Manhattan Bank until his recent retirement? David Rockefeller.[†] Therefore, it appears that David Rockefeller helped determine policies for the U.S. banks and the World Bank. It also seems apparent that Russia could not have established itself as a major political and military power under different banking/lending policies.

The connection weaves from political and monetary desire, to manipulation, corporate control, power, and world domination. Is the love of money the root of all evil? It might be. Politics does not work without financial control. It is clear throughout history that control of the people requires control of the purse strings.

The Antichrist who will proclaim himself to be God and who will have the ability to prevent buying and selling will be the one who controls all the finances. Finances and materialism are almost inseparable, and restraints on either will be difficult to accept. The countries that will be hit the hardest are those that are heavily

---

[*]As recently as October 1988, the Kremlin avoided releasing information regarding Russia's international debt, monetary reserves, or interest payments by claiming that doing so would "cause economic harm." The confidentiality did not hamper securing additional loans.

[†]David Rockefeller summed up his significance on the world monetary scene by claiming in a August 5, 1974 *Wall Street Journal* interview, to be the most important [powerful] banker in the world.

materialistic. All people are materialistic throughout the world, with the very poorest, the least, perhaps. But one thing is abundantly clear: Great materialism is affecting the entire Earth's population, and whoever can control that materialism will control the world. It is also clear that controlling world finances efficiently will require a high level of automation.

AUTOMATION

To understand how 666 relates to this discussion, one needs to explore technology. One pertinent contributor to this technology is the International Business Machines Corporation. IBM developed a laser method of information transfer that has now become universally accepted. Lasers are used for many different applications in society today, such as measuring distances, detecting structural flaws, determining straightness, and so forth. You can see the IBM system at your local supermarket quickly reading prices and controlling inventory as it prints out a list of all purchased items. Since checkers no longer have to punch keys on a register, check-out time and errors are reduced. This system also provides the shopper with an itemized receipt. That receipt information is stored in a central computer, which keeps inventory and indicates what products the store should order, as well as which products should no longer be carried.

But the use of automation is going considerably further. In fact, in Fresno, California, one of eight regional test cities, a new computer system called Behavior Scan gives shoppers a bar code card that is read at each purchase. The computer then keeps a detailed list of all purchases made by a family, including brands and quantity of each product. This same computer is also attached to the user's home television set to monitor what is being watched. It then selects commercials to be shown to that customer to affect his specific buying habits. While most customers claim that they are not affected by these commercials, the advertising companies have spent a lot of money on research proving otherwise. Is this the start of a more modern version of George Orwell's *1984* or the complete control depicted in Vance Packard's *The Hidden Persuaders* ?

Certainly, computers are powerful and indispensable tools. Thanks to computers, paychecks are deposited automatically into checking and savings accounts at predefined rates while many bills and loans are automatically paid on time every month. The system works so well that many institutions give a discount on loans and insurance payments if automatic payment is used (they are more confident that they will be paid and on time). This can conveniently save time, postage, and worry.* The world is positioned to facilitate the ever growing requirements for increased automation and convenience.

The convenience of computers is everywhere. Even a simple, inexpensive $3 watch contains a computer. No longer does it merely tell time; it also can add and subtract, keep time in three different zones, give the day and the date, and beep at predetermined intervals. Computerized voices in fancy cars warn you if you have not fastened your seat belt, that your oil is low, or that you are almost out of fuel. The proliferation of computers has created a strong dependence on them, for real need and pure convenience. The average American's name is accessed 35 times a day by computer,[11] and this is only the beginning as we become plugged into the ever-growing system.

Our credit card system is also very convenient. Carrying cash is unnecessary and sometimes useless, for example, when renting a car or cashing a check. With a credit card, transactions are easier, and banks are now able (and more then willing), to deduct payment of your credit card bill automatically from your main account.

In fact, paper money soon may become a thing of the past for three reasons:

1. The government is concerned about the advances being made in color xerographic technology. Advanced copy machines will soon be able to produce counterfeit bills

---

*The paperless, or fully electronic, office is a reality. General Motors claims that it saves millions of dollars annually with its new paperless office system. The system controls 20,000 suppliers and $4 billion per month.

that are indistinguishable from government issues. The FBI reported that up to 20 percent of people having access to advanced color copiers will produce some counterfeit bills.

2.   The successful introduction of the Smart Card in France and U.S. test cities such as Washington, D.C., and Norfolk, Virginia, may render cash obsolete. This Smart Card, manufactured by Motorola and Toshiba, carries a complete history of the user, including a physical description and health record. The card allows direct payment to the seller by instantaneously deducting the purchase amount and any service charges directly from the cardholder's account. Thus, not only is the seller paid immediately but, also, the card companies save millions of dollars by eliminating bad payments and personal bankruptcy debts. Reducing credit card fraud should also save card companies large sums of money. For example, MasterCard could save $25 million annually by eliminating fraudulent cards. By the end of 1990, 20 million fraud-resistant cards will be in use in France. Seventeen other countries have agreed to a standard card for all bank machines. Visa, Eurocheque, Eurocard, and MasterCard have already agreed to a method to make their cards, systems, and money access interchangeable. Thus by eliminating checks and voluntary payments, the credit card industry would save 3.2 billion dollars per year.[*]

3.   The Federal Government is paying close attention to methods for taxing the $300 billion underground economy in the United States. Unreported income costs the U.S. Treasury $90 billion per year. If cash were eliminated, computers could keep track of all income.

---

[*]Evidence that cards may soon replace cash (and checks) was provided by Arco service stations and Lucky supermarkets, which announced in September 1986 that their pumps and check-out stands now accept automatic teller bank cards. With this system, payment is deducted electronically from the user's bank account before the user receives his purchase. Within one month, 6,400 service stations and supermarkets in 23 states were fitted with the system.

The gentlemen who came up with the laser reader in supermarkets for IBM also invented the means of placing the same kind of bar code beneath living tissue in one-billionth of a second. This marking is totally invisible to the naked eye, and it can be read only by a certain type of laser. The writing and reading is totally harmless and painless. The inventors demonstrated this system in 1979 by marking salmon as they swam downstream. The fish were totally unaware of the process as the laser burned a code into their flesh. The computer then keeps track of the codes. Years later, these fish will be detected by the same system as they swim back upstream and are forced through fish ladders and chutes.

Just as impressive is what Walter Wriston, the chairman of CitiCorp, did in 1983. He passed a rule within the bank that was later withdrawn as a result of public outcry. This rule stated that unless you were a depositor of $5,000 or more, you were not entitled to a teller.[12] This meant that the vast majority of depositors would have to stand in line outside the bank and "talk" to machines. This was an economic move, of course, because banks have had some problems of late. But its message was that people would no longer talk to people. If banks could establish such a policy, then they could make the minimum deposit higher and higher. Finally, everything for everyone would be done by machines. The concern is that we are reaching a highly automated state, which if followed to the next logical step might have profound impacts on how we rate life.

Even more startling was an "off the cuff" statement made by an other chairman of an eastern megabank: He announced that a method is in place that can imprint in human hands a silicon chip the size of the head of a pin.[13] That chip will include not only the person's identification number, Social Security number, name, and birthplace, but also his criminal background, educational level, financial worth in the community, and his political affiliations.*

---

*Such a system is currently manufactured by Taymar, Inc., Westminster, CO. The U.S. Agriculture Department uses the product for cattle. Will it be used for people in the future?

With such a system, the minute someone walked through the door of the bank, he would be sensed and the bank would know who he was, where he came from, what he did, and how much he was worth. All this would occur before a person could reach the counter.

Now this was one step further than even progressive thinkers envisioned. There had been discussions about placing codes on the hand to be used as identification marks, like fingerprints, similar to package bar codes in supermarkets. With such a system, you would not need cash or a validated check or even a Smart Card. You could put your hand through a laser and be read by the computer. The store would automatically deduct the amount of the purchase from your account. The method would be efficient in terms of cost, speed, thoroughness, and elimination of bad checks.* But the price of all this automation is individual independence from nameless bureaucrats looking over your shoulder and approving (allowing) every transaction.

The amount of control would be unprecedented: however, the government would immediately know how to put this control to use. People would no longer be able to cheat the government because every time anyone had any money, the government would know about it. The government could collect taxes each time you spent your money, and, thus, there would be no more filing on April 15th. It also means that advanced printing and photocopying machines could not be used for counterfeiting. Even a law breaker who traded with stolen goods would have his purchase and sale traced by computer as he tried to move or "spend" funds. The government would monitor every transaction, knowing precisely everyone's location, actions, and worth. Instant evaluations, approval or disapproval, and tax deductions on every individual would be made.

---

*Such systems are not in the distant future. Six thousand people in Sweden have accepted a mark on their right hands in a test of a totally cashless society. Tests also have been conducted in Japan and the Dominican Republic in Latin America.

Small wonder that the government likes this idea. Governments have always liked control. They would like to control everything, even the areas they say they do not want to control, such as business, transportation, education, religion, entertainment, and other governments. If this sounds the least bit exaggerated, just look at our government's actions regarding the restrictions of business concerning tax credit, labor laws, advertising, antitrust laws, and corporate subsidies. Even in deregulation, transportation requires licensing, registration, inspection, subsidies, price controls, flight approval, and government flight controllers. Although there may be talk of eliminating the Federal Department of Education, there is no attempt to reduce control of school curriculum, subsidies, and even school lunches. Most universities are dependent on federal aid and research grants.

The government controls religion by granting tax exemption to "desired religions" and by making it illegal to pray in school. The government exercises control of entertainment by licensing and/or censoring television, radio, movies, and books. The Federal Government also seeks to control other governments by rewarding or threatening them with trade concessions, military or economic aid, sanctions, or war. The highest people in government, it would seem, want the government to have total control of everything.

In Orwell's *1984*, the government "took over," and everyone was controlled by "Big Brother." In reality, government may take over, not through control of transportation and censorship, but through the economy, the lending institutions, and every financial transaction. Is it too far-fetched to imagine that you may have to take a mark on your hand to be able to buy and sell and exist in a modern society? The technology exists. The chairman of the megabank was asked what it would take to motivate people to put little pieces of silicon under their skin. He answered, "a major catastrophe." He knew people would not do it voluntarily.

Of course if there was a financial or national emergency (catastrophe), the government would exercise unprecedented control, and compliance of citizens would be anything but voluntary.

BANKING

Rapid change has not by-passed the banking industry. The high interest rates of the early 1980s and bad investments[*] were responsible for the collapse of more banks in 1983 than were lost since the Great Depression. In fact, for 30 years after the Depression, virtually no banks failed in America. But things are changing. The height of bank failures during the Great Depression was in 1938, with 84 closures. By comparison, collapses numbered two in 1945, three in 1960, and nine by 1980. In 1988 a staggering 205 banks collapsed, including thousands of branches. Presently, 1,500 banks are on the Fed's problem list, with half listed as already insolvent. These collapses have caused a host of banks to be absorbed by bigger banks, whose size and diversity allowed them to handle the short term downside while anticipating the long term potential of such acquisitions. However, problem banks now overwhelm banks strong enough to absorb them.

Who controls the interest rate? The Federal Reserve Board does. Oddly enough, the Fed is not a part of the Federal Government. This body, which has such a major impact on interest rate, money supply, inflation, and bank success, does not answer to the President of the United States or to the Congress. Instead, it is made up of and controlled by bankers—big bankers! And they are obviously influenced by the five biggest banks in America.

Is it unreasonable to believe that those five big banks may have learned something from the oil industry? Remember that David Rockefeller was chairman of the Board of Chase Manhattan Bank and that the Rockefellers controlled Standard Oil, which at one time controlled 95 percent of all the oil produced in America. Look at what happened during the oil embargo. To this day, government investigators cannot figure out whether there really

---

[*]Partial bank deregulation allowed banks to seek larger profits through risky investments. This practice, however, placed bank equity and deposits at risk. For example, on October 19, 1987, many big New York banks lost 30 percent of their equity because of the stock market crash. Still, banks are pushing Congress for a full repeal of the Glass-Steagall Act. The act, which prohibits banks from underwriting securities, was passed because of bank failures during the Great Depression.

was an oil shortage. What is known is that suddenly the big oil companies rid themselves of the competing independents in all areas that were marginal and somehow emerged out of this crisis with greatly increased profits.

Could that same mentality of the 1973 and 1979 oil shortages have influenced banking? Is it possible that the big banks made money tight to make interest rates rise to unprecedented levels? Could the banks (while causing a worldwide recession) have been trying to crush the smaller independents and to improve their own long term profits? Might not this plan still be maturing as banks are forced to increase reserves? As banks become shaky, they are acquired by bigger, more diversified banks. The new chairman of the Fed, Alan Greenspan, speaks of a vision of "five superbanks." Does he envision that when the dust settles only five banks will be left? Will they be the same five banks that now make up the cornerstone of the Federal Reserve System?

THE FEDERAL RESERVE

Since the Federal Reserve System is not part of the Federal Government, some contend that the agency is illegal and unconstitutional. The Fed exercises enormous power as it sets interest rates (by lending money to other banks at varying rates of interest), changes the money supply (by making more money available to banks for loans), sells government bonds, and dictates how much reserves banks must have. Indeed, this power is so great that it has been accused of controlling the election of presidents.[*] The Fed is the only bank in America that has **never** been audited or investigated by Congress or any other agency.[14] To appreciate how the little understood Fed became so powerful, one must examine its beginnings.

The ultimate power of financial control was well recognized by those who wanted to accomplish in America what the Rothschilds had done in Europe. John D. Rockefeller was one

---

[*]The Fed controls the money supply and thus controls the extent of economic growth or recession. When the money supply is high, incumbent parties are reelected. When the money supply is tight, the incumbent party is ousted.

such opportunist. Being the world's richest man was not enough for him.

Because of his past actions, he was increasingly enmeshed in legal battles. Public discontent resulting from his abuse of the "little guy" caused his advisors to recommend spending large sums of money on a publicity campaign to change his image. Otherwise, he would have to face the growing possibility of being assassinated by a crazed member of the outraged public. Following this advice, he acted the role of the philanthropist. First, he publicly donated $600,000 to start the University of Chicago.*[6]

But what he craved was not an institute of higher learning but rather power—power over the central bank of the United States. Of course the United States had no Central Bank and the Constitution makes no provision for one, but that was not to foil the son of a traveling con-artist. Because public sentiment was still so anti-Rockefeller, he could not have legislation passed that seemed connected to him, his banks, or even a Central Bank. To avoid fears of creating a Central Bank, he had a respectable professor at the University of Chicago coauthor a bill with some bribed senators to establish the Federal Reserve Board. The result was that the power and the profits of the Central Bank of the United States became his.

As evidence of the power and profits involved, consider the following excerpt:[14]

> In order to cover its expenses, the government is forced to borrow....Each week the Secretary of the Treasury authorizes the issuance of Treasury bills, notes or bonds. These government securities are placed for sale with the Federal Reserve through its Open Market operation in New York.

---

*Rockefeller had a long history of making private religious contributions. The new strategy was to make large public contributions, for example, culminating in over $40 million being donated to the University of Chicago.

When the Federal Reserve decides to buy the government securities, it simply creates the funds out of nothing...it has the Department of Printing and Engraving print up sufficient currency to cover the cost*...this becomes part of the National Debt....

The taxpayers are then required to pay interest to a private bank for the privilege of allowing that bank to order worthless paper money (with no backing) from the Department of Printing and to lend it back to the government that created the Fed and printed the money. Of course, along with the interest, the principal must also be paid back to the Fed, even though the principal belonged to the government (people) in the first place!

At the instigation of the big banks, Congress passed...the Depository Institutions Deregulation and Monetary Control Act, Public Law 96-221. This new law greatly increased the power of the Federal Reserve, yet few members of the Congress were aware of its dangerous implications. Under the new law the Fed can monetize (turn into money) all sorts of debt instruments, including debts of foreign governments...the Fed can literally print money or grant credit—using that foreign debt as security—then re-route the money to the lending banks to make current interest and principal payments....The Fed has used foreign debt as collateral for issuing Federal Reserve Notes on at least 139 occasions....[15]

Who owns the Fed? The answer will tell us who controls the country. The Federal Reserve Bank of New York [when it was first established], issued 203,053 shares. On May 19, 1914, the Bank told the Comptroller of the

---

*When the Fed orders currency, it pays the Department of Printing and Engraving only for the expense of the paper and ink: about $0.0015 for each $1, $10, or $100 dollar bill.

Currency that the big New York banks had taken [bought] more than half of them. The Rockefeller National City Bank took the largest number of shares: 30,000. Morgan's First National Bank took 15,000 shares. When these two banks merged in 1955, they owned almost a quarter of the shares of the New York Fed, which controls the system. The Chase National Bank, also a Rockefeller entity took 6,000 shares....

As of July 26, 1983, the official Rockefeller banks (Chase Manhattan and CitiBank) held almost 30 percent of the shares of the New York Fed.[16]

Paul A. Volcker, was appointed chairman of the Federal Reserve Board by President Jimmy Carter in 1979, and was reappointed by President Reagan.

Volcker had been President of the New York Federal Reserve Bank, and has held management positions at David Rockefeller's Chase Manhattan Bank, is a trustee of the Rockefeller Foundation, and a board member of Rockefeller's Council on Foreign Relations.[15]

The extent of the Fed's control of the country was expressed by U.S. Congressman Louis McFadden, chairman of the House Banking and Currency Committee investigating the crash of 1929: "It was not accidental. It was a carefully contrived occurrence...."[17] The investigation found that the major New York banks jointly liquidated their extensive stock holdings and placed their assets into gold and silver, where their value was protected by law. Then in October 1929 the financiers started calling in broker loans. Since almost all stock was heavily margined, stockholders were forced to sell. But with loans being called, there were few buyers; therefore, prices fell. Each drop in stock value was followed by an automatic sale of margined stock at an even more depressed price. As the crash of the stock market damaged businesses and 25 percent of the work force lost jobs, the banks called in business loans and personal mortgages. The foreclosures bought American assets for pennies on the dollar. When the depression was over, the major banks had gained control of almost every important industry in America.[14]

CENTRAL COMPUTING

As mentioned earlier, the impact of computers on society has been enormous. However, their likely future role may be overwhelming. As powerful as computers are, their effectiveness is greatly multiplied when they can communicate with other computers. For example, missile launch command computers talk to U.S. Weather Bureau computers to update the possible flight paths of thousands of Minuteman missiles every hour. Thus, to enhance a system's capabilities, computers need to talk to computers. To sort out the enormous amount of cross-references, a central computer is needed.

The central computer for America is in Texas, and the international computer that ties all the national central computers together is situated in Brussels, Belgium. The Brussels computer is housed in a 13 story building, the first three floors of which are occupied totally by this system's hardware. Because of its size, the Brussels computer is referred to affectionately as "the Beast."

This immense computer has enough capacity to store every detail about the lives of every human being on Earth, the information contained in the Library of Congress, and every book ever printed. Having operated for years, it stores a growing volume of information as additional countries tie into it ever more heavily. This allows international banking, interstate banking, and quick credit references. Money can be moved from New York to California or London in minutes. If a deposit is made in a bank other than where the check was drawn, banks usually impose a 5- to 10-day holding period. Actually, this practice is just a means for banks to increase their "float" and thus to increase their profits, since the money is transferred within one day. What happens to the money for the other days? The bank uses it to float short term loans by which the bank earns interest.[*] Banks typically wait longer to issue credit because they want to use the money for as many days as possible.

Daily manipulation of funds by banks is common. Many banks are forced to move their funds around the globe with the sun to have their reserves where they are needed—in the banks that are open.[†] Even the CIA likes the capability of the central computer because it can check on personnel mobility, foreign trading, and all financial transactions.

Many advanced computers are available with many designations, but one is especially interesting. NCR produced a six-core memory computer with 60 bytes per word in conjunction with six bits to the character.[19] It is named and advertised as the 6-60-6, which defines the size and shape of the computer. The only way this can be pronounced is six sixty-six (666). In computer language, 666 has a unique significance.

A computer is an information retrieval system, and all of its information is stored as numbers. A computer's memory cell has only two states—on and off, or mathematically 1 and 0. Thus, every number must be represented in 1s and 0s. We use a decimal system based on 10; thus, it has 10 symbols: 0, 1, 2, 3, 4, 5, 6, 7, 8, and 9. Computers use a binary system using two symbols (0 and 1). To manage large numbers, computers use a binary coded decimal system (BCD), which consists of groups of four digits, to make up all numbers. By comparing the groups of numbers listed below one can find each system's equivalent symbol. Thus, 0001, 0011, 0111, 0101 in the binary coded decimal system is equal to our decimal system number 1,375.

---

[*] Banks earn as much as $1 million a day on floats.

[†] Trillions of dollars a day are moved by wire transfer. Banks commonly have $125 billion in "daylight overdrafts" in anticipation of receiving payments in time to "balance" their books at closing.[18]

Decimal System		Binary System
0	=	0000
1	=	0001
2	=	0010
3	=	0011
4	=	0100
5	=	0101
6	=	0110
7	=	0111
8	=	1000
9	=	1001

(For various reasons, some computers use Base 8 (0-7) and therefore do not use the last two symbols shown.)

As shown in the BCD system, the number 6 is represented by 0110. This is unique because 0110 written backwards or upside-down is still 0110. The only other number in the BCD system with the same property is its complement 1001, or 9. (However, not every computer counts past 7.) This consistency is the same in every country in the world, unaffected by language because every computer speaks the same language of "1s" and "0s." Thus, 0110, 0110, 0110 is 666 universally.

In the Book of Revelation, John said that 666 is the mark of the beast. This number also represents the universal consistency of the computers that will be required to control the world's finances and thus the world's people. When John wrote 1,900 years ago, he did not know anything about the binary number system, computers, or why computers would require binary coded decimals. Yet, he stated emphatically that the mark of the beast is 666.

Is this to say that the endtime beast is merely a building located in Belgium? No! The Brussels computer is no more the beast than a general is an army. The significance is that computerization for financial dominance is the financial beast. The beast is a false god and the worship of that false god. Worship means "worth respect." A false god does not have to assume the figure of a man: It is the physical representation of that which controls, that which is worshipped. So, if people worship the "$" symbol too much for what it can acquire, influence, or accomplish, then that can qualify it as the false god. The Brussels computer is only the figurehead of a vast, soon-to-be indispensable financial network that will control all financial transactions and thus all businesses and people.

He who controls the system controls all. What is feared by some is that whoever is in control will demand that all take the code (mark) on their hand to be able to buy and sell. Money, credit cards, and checkbooks would be totally eliminated. Everything would be done through the government, through computer, giving the government total control. The greatest fear is that when receiving the mark, you also may be forced to pledge allegiance to your flag and (as in the days of kings) to your ruler, but in this case the world leader would be the Antichrist. Of course, to have allegiance with the Antichrist is to make a pact with the Devil. If you think that this unified system is very far away, then you have missed some intriguing news items.

As you probably are aware, the government has been talking about a national identification number for some time.* It is supposed to make record keeping easier and to provide a means of crosschecking. It will help find deserting husbands who owe child support as well as locate tax evaders. Most people anticipate that the Social Security number will play a part in this national identification code.

The government's system for identification uses 18 digits, the last nine of which are the Social Security number. Virtually every citizen in the country over the age of 1 will be forced to have a Social Security number. At present, a Social Security number is necessary to have a job or a savings/checking account. Starting in

---

*The nation moved closer to a mandatory personal identification number on November 6, 1986, when President Reagan signed a law requiring all American citizens to provide federal identification (i.e., passport/Social Security number) within 24 hours of accepting a job.

1990, every child over one year old must have a Social Security number to qualify as a dependent on tax returns. Preceding this 9-digit Social Security number are 3 digits corresponding to one's telephone area code. Obviously, the whole world is tied by phone; even barren deserts with no inhabitants have area codes. In front of these numbers is a country code; for America it is 110. From this single, universally consistent number, the government will instantly know a person's country, region, and identity. Does that seem logical so far? But that accounts for only 15 digits, and the system is based on 18. The missing 3-digit code specifies that you are in the system: 666.

All computerized companies are going to 18-digit identification codes. According to the report *666 Is Here,*[19] Sears Roebuck is going on this system and is committed to changing over all its credit cards. J.C. Penney's is reported to be switching over, as well as New York Telephone. The U.S. Government used to prefix all the serial numbers of everything it owned with the code 451. But that also is changing; the dog tags on every soldier in America are to be converted to 666.[19]

Is that enough to concern you? The point is that 666 is a significant and important part of what the future is going to hold. The Bible prophesied it. Nostradamus explained it, and we are presently at the very edge of seeing it become enacted. Rumors abound about people receiving checks with these marks, governments admit they need better financial control, and the chairman of one of the largest banks says, "It's ready; we just need a major catastrophe."

BANKING STABILITY

Let us examine what kind of catastrophe this megabank chairman may have been referring to (or planning for) to justify implementation. The financial system of the Free World is on the verge of a major catastrophe. In fact, it almost collapsed in the summer of 1983, and the U.S. Government Printing Office was ready to print "new" money in case it did.[20]

This problem started when the Arabs put tons of money into our banks because they had a surplus of funds from selling us all the oil we bought at record high prices. The money was not backed by gold or silver, but only by faith in the U.S. dollar to be stable and universally accepted in trade. Banks could not afford to pay interest on all this deposited foreign money if it just stayed idle in their vaults—they needed some big borrowers—so they lent it to a variety of Third World countries, such as Mexico, Argentina, Brazil, and Poland. Because of the recession that developed, these countries could not pay back even the interest, which in the case of Mexico is $10 billion per year. We keep refinancing their loans so that they will not default. They never see the majority of any additional money, since interest payments that are past due are simply deducted from the handout. Of course, the next time the payment is due the interest will be even greater, as will the inability to pay it back. The problem is that if a debtor country defaults or nationalizes its debt, the banks will stand to lose unprecedented sums of money.

Many times countries have nationalized businesses and debts. In such a move, the government declares companies or notes owned by foreigners to be henceforth owned by the nation. The government then just takes them over, and the former owners lose their assets and all claims to them. Sometimes 10 cents on the dollar is paid for their holdings, and other times the government just takes over outright. Other countries cannot do much about it since it is not worth starting a war. A war would not retrieve the lost money, but would cost additional large sums of cash. The most a country can do is threaten never to trade with the nationalizing country again. However, such action would only further damage both nations. The nations still would trade, but probably only on a cash only basis for several years.

A severe problem could arise: If any of these Third World nations defaulted, the banks themselves would no longer have assets to cover the deposits made in their banks.* Therefore, they would not be solvent, and they would have to close outright or suffer a run. In either case, people would not be able to get their

---

*Of America's 11 largest banks, nine have loaned 277 percent of their equity to Third World and Soviet-bloc nations and therefore cannot withstand a major default.

money.* Do not count on the FDIC or FSLIC to come to the rescue. Both are underfinanced, and each lost billions of dollars in 1988. Before the FSLIC can be of help, President Bush will have to help it find $100 billion in needed bailout funds. Over 500 banks have recently failed. For the most part, these were small, independent banks with bad farm, oil, and real-estate loans secured by the assets of the land itself. The noteworthy exception was Continental Illinois Bank, which in 1985 required a bailout of over $7.5 billion and additional guarantees to depositors to save it from collapse until a bigger bank could be found (forced) to buy it.†

The FDIC has always had the charter of stopping isolated local bank runs by dumping money into the local bank of need. But the total cash reserve is equal to only 1 percent of the money deposited in the member banks. If 2 percent of the banks had a run at the same time, there would be little the FDIC could do to stop the banks from closing and the depositors from losing their savings. If 2 percent of the banks closed suddenly, the other 98 percent of the banks would also have a run and would have to close, causing all depositors to lose. Of course, if the banks collapsed, the whole economy of the United States and the world would go into total turmoil. All financial markets would collapse with the banks. The October 1987 stock market crash would seem mild by comparison. Instead of losing 500 points (one year's gain), the market could drop to a level of 500. As the New York and American exchanges fell, so would markets around the world. Confidence in America would diminish causing foreigners to pull their deposits and investments from "the world's most stable country."

---

*During the Great Depression, 9,000 banks declared bank holidays and simply suspended operations. In the more recent Ohio and Maryland State Bank failures, depositors did not lose their money—they were just denied access to it for years.

†The value of failed bank assets is sobering. In December 1988, Revlon bought a chain of failing Texas S&Ls claiming $12 billion in assets, for $.3 billion plus a guarantee that Revlon would be repaid for the first $5 billion of additional losses. In August of the same year, the FDIC put $4 billion into a different Texas bank and sold controlling interest in it for $210 million only after giving the buyer a $700 million tax break.

In an attempt to reduce the impact, the government would resort to some drastic measures.* The first action would be to print billions and billions of dollars to give to the banks to pay back the loans for those other countries. In that case, inflation would accelerate so rapidly that it would be almost impossible to track. Protecting the banks from collapse would cause money to be worth virtually nothing. And if you think that we did not come very close to that happening, you are wrong. If you think that it cannot still happen, you are wrong again.[†]

All it would take to collapse the world's financial system is the realization that paper money is only paper. After all, that is all it is. It has no intrinsic value, unlike something that can be used, manufactured, or eaten. Most wealth is not even in the form of money anymore; it is represented by a piece of paper (deposit slip) that a bank gives you symbolizing the wealth you gave to it. Since the bank lent your money to someone else, it cannot return it to you anymore. The person who borrowed your money from your bank bought something, and the person (or company) who sold it to him put the money (not the goods) in some other bank and received another paper deposit slip. That bank immediately lent the money to someone else. Today in America every paper dollar is claimed by at least six sources: the person who deposited it, the bank, the person who sold something to the borrower of the money from the bank, this third person's bank, the person who borrowed from the second bank, and the person who sold goods

---

*The term "government" is intended to include Congress, whose approval is required for all money bills. Recall, however, that Congress did approve the Chrysler bailout loans. If the crisis is important enough, Congress will exercise untested (untraditional) power. Whether such actions are constitutional is another matter.

†The IRS is so concerned about massive reductions of taxable revenue that it passed a law in January 1989 stating that losses caused by the failure of a nonfederally insured bank or savings institution in excess of $10,000 cannot be counted as losses on income tax returns. Federally insured accounts will technically not be lost—just frozen without interest or access. By the time enough money is printed to allow full payment, inflation will have made the principal worthless. Since the principal will be eventually returned, no loss can be claimed as a tax deduction.

or services to the second bank's borrower.* Therefore, it is physically impossible for everyone in the country (and the world) who thinks he has money in the bank to take it out and put it under his mattress on the same night, even if there were no bad debts, no foreclosures, no late payments, and no debtors in default.

Do not be lulled into a feeling of false security by bank ads that claim to be "$8 billion dollars strong" or "$8 billion safe." If banks did not need more cash, they would not be advertising for your deposit. Examine one large savings and loan that is one of the most secure banks in America today, claiming "over $8 billion in assets." However, its balance sheet also shows over $8 billion in liabilities. Most of its assets are in long-term mortgage loans.

Assume that no home loans go into default, there are no bad debts, and California never has a severe earthquake that destroys a large percentage of the homes this bank has mortgaged. Then the total assets of the bank would be only 2 percent greater than its liabilities, with enough cash (not counting securities, stocks, and bonds) to cover 6.5 percent of its depositors. Further assume the bank could quickly sell every building, every bank, and every typewriter it has for full market value on short notice and reduce its payroll, insurance, and taxes to zero. Even under these conditions, this bank could barely pay back 7 percent of its depositors if the people who gave the bank their money wanted it back tomorrow. If all of the bank's securities, bonds, and stocks could be liquidated within a short term without having their value affected by the crisis, then another 17 percent of the depositors could get their money in the near term (but not today). The rest of the depositors would have to wait for loans and long-term mortgages to be paid off over the next few decades to get all their money back.[†]

---

*Under present laws controlling the level of reserves, the theoretical maximum is $12 of credit for every dollar deposited.

[†]If a banking crisis occurred, it would be unlikely that any banking institution would be capable of lending the needed capital to repay depositors. The likelihood of such loans is further reduced because if they were available, their rates of interest would be much higher than the rates of the outstanding loans; thus, money would be lost in such transactions.

That would be the outcome under the best conditions. In the worst case, a bank may have 10 to 20 percent of its assets in paper IOUs with poor Third World nations that cannot or will not pay it back. Then there would be no hope of ever paying back all the depositors, and the bank would close. The Feds would come in and try to find a buyer with enough assets to back it up. This works with isolated cases where there is still a potential for profits, but if Third World countries nationalize their debts, all the banks would be affected. Some of the very biggest banks would fall the hardest.

The total indebtedness of Third World countries is over $1 trillion. Latin America alone owes over $410 billion, of which over $100 billion is owed to U.S. banks. The gravity of the problem is clear. The FDIC has 1,355 banks on its problem list, and the big banks are scrambling to salvage billions of dollars in loans to developing countries. A default by a major debtor nation such as Brazil or Argentina could cause a massive banking collapse. The Federal Deposit Insurance Corporation has only $15 billion in reserves to help failed banks[21], which is less than 1 percent of the amount insured. If the 1,355 problem banks were to fail to the tune of $12 million per bank, the entire FDIC fund would be wiped out. Actually, the problem is much more severe, since $12 million in bailout money is not realistic. Remember, it took $7.5 billion to "strengthen" Continental Illinois Bank to end its "run" and another $1.5 billion to cover other losses. If this one bank had collapsed, there may have been precious little, if anything at all, left in the $15 billion FDIC insurance fund.

One way to solve the problem is to have every man, woman, and child in America send $1,650 to South America to pay off its debt ($4,000 each for the Third World debt). In fact, it may come to that as the United States tries to prevent "defaults." In July 1983, the U.S. Treasury agreed to be substituted for the Bank of International Settlement (BIS) for delayed payments on $500 million owed by Brazil after that country missed its second deadline. Similar guarantees have also been made regarding Polish debt payments. Many Third World nations are already technically in default, but the hope is that bankers can conceal it for another 10 years so that they can better deal with it. As stated in *The Wall Street Journal*, June 14, 1983, "Western institutions don't really believe they will really ever see any Polish loans repaid, but have an interest in putting off the day they actually write off the loans.... It's now come down merely to a game we are playing with numbers."

Of the $410 billion lent to Latin America, 63 percent came from commercial banks. Debt repudiation is becoming a term increasingly used in Latin America, which can spell devastating results for Western banks. Consider five major debtor nations:

1. Mexico was the model debtor after taking severe austerity steps to reduce its $105 billion debt. However, unexpected problems have diminished this position. Oil prices and oil sales are down, thus limiting Mexico's ability to repay its loans. Mexico's $10 billion a year interest payment is difficult in good years, and impossible in bad years. Mexico's *peso* is pegged to the dollar, but even with a 40-percent drop in the U.S. dollar, the Mexican economy could not maintain stability. On November 18, 1987, the *peso* was devalued by 55 percent against the already weak dollar, setting off financial panic. Inflation increased by 50 percent in one day and by 10 thousand percent in five years. Mexico's banking system is so unstable that it has trouble selling 7-day treasury bills at an interest rate of 350 percent per year. If Mexico's recession continues or if interest rates rise, the situation will become even worse.

    The solution? Throw more good money after bad. As of July 22, 1986, Mexico received an additional $12 billion in loans from 500 commercial banks that already hold $100 billion in Mexican notes and $1 trillion in Third World IOUs. Mexico also received some other benefits that make other borrowers envious:

   • If the price of oil drops below $9 per barrel, Mexico automatically receives extra loans.

   • If the Mexican economy does not grow by 3 percent per year (which is more than U.S. growth), Mexico will automatically receive additional loans. These additional loans seem certain since Mexico's present growth rate is a negative 4 percent.

2. Argentina has a $50-billion outstanding debt and is actively seeking $1.1 billion in new loans. Argentina has an inflation rate that bounces between 100 and 1,000 percent. Unemployment is over 50 percent, and a recession has cut deeply into its tax revenues. Even though Argentina has received a 12-year extension on its debt payments, political advocates are campaigning for repudiation of its foreign debt.

3. Peru has a $15-billion outstanding debt. President Garcia reduced debt payments to 10 percent of export earnings. Peru is asking for its debt to be stretched out for an additional 25 years at 3 percent interest. Peru also requested a 5-year grace period before any payments are due on its $15 billion debt. This, of course, would amount to a substantial write-down. Like other nations, Peru is actively seeking additional IMF loans.

4. Venezuela has a $35-billion outstanding debt. Half of its payments came from oil exports. With the recent reduction in oil prices and sales, only the expected $2.8 billion in new loans will prevent default.

5. Brazil has a $121-billion outstanding debt and is looking for $16 billion in short term credit. Inflation hovers at 1,000 percent per year. Brazil gave the banking community a major scare in February 1987 by announcing a debt moratorium on 80 percent of its debt. Although Brazil and Western banks believed (correctly), that the moratorium would be for only six to nine months, it caused the banks to change the way in which they report Brazil's nonperforming loans. U.S. law prohibits a country that has openly declared a moratorium from being granted new loans to cover up its nonpayment. Thus, banks could no longer call the entire Brazilian loan an asset, and the banking community suffered record-breaking losses.[*]

---

[*] In an attempt to improve public opinion, banks chose to call the situation not a "write down of assets," but rather, "an increase in reserves." A rather interesting term since the banks have much less in reserve now to protect depositors than before.

CitiCorp may have been anticipating the Brazilian difficulty for some time; it has been selling off Brazilian debt to other banks for 80 cents on the dollar for years. Why sell its assets for only 80 percent of their value? To avoid the alternative, which may be to receive only 20 percent of their value when the problem worsens.* CitiCorp was the first to announce a $1.2-billion increase in reserves and a subsequent $1-billion loss (later updated as shown below). Many other banks were forced to follow CitiCorp's lead and increase their reserves. The main difference is that CitiCorp had been providing for this situation for years, whereas the other banks were less prepared. Some leading banks and their losses for the second quarter of 1987 are listed below:

Bank	Loss
CitiCorp	$2.6 billion
Manufacturers	1.4 billion
Chemical	1.1 billion
B of A	1.0 billion
Mellon	570 million
Bankers Trust	550 million
First Inter	470 million
Marine Midland	300 million
Wells Fargo	294 million

Even worse, the banks had additional complications. To prevent other nations from joining Brazil in a moratorium that would collapse the banking system, the banks guaranteed additional loans to other South American nations and reduced requirements associated with older loans. The banks were trying to tighten austerity measures in Latin America in an attempt to reduce the need for additional loans. All of these actions cost money and actually increase the amount the banks will lose when the collapse eventually occurs. To bring Brazil back in line, it was granted an additional $11.5-billion loan.

---

*The situation has worsened. Mexican and Brazilian loans are now traded for 50 cents on the dollar, while Peruvian loans claim only 13 cents.

The five nations listed are not the only ones with major debt problems. Indonesia, Nigeria, and Ecuador have debts large enough to jeopardize the world banking system. Even nations whose foreign debts (to the United States) are not large enough to cause a banking collapse have an absurd opinion of U.S. loans:

1. Prime Minister Shimon Peres of Israel proposed that the United States give $30 billion in aid to oil-producing nations in the Middle East to strengthen their economies, which were hurt by the slash in oil prices. These are the same nations that formed the unconscionable price-fixing ring that raised prices in the first place. This, in turn, caused conservation and increased oil exploration and eventual oversupply. Apparently, the Arabs did not get all of America's money, and so the United States should send them a check for the rest.

2. President Hosni Mubarak of Egypt, after receiving $110 million in emergency debt assistance, asked the United States to relieve Egypt's debt of $4.6 billion. The $4.6 billion is over and above the $20.3 billion the United States has given in economic and military aid for signing the 1978 Camp David Accords.[22]

   The question of arming Arabs aside, consider the possibility of Egypt ever paying back its $35 billion debt to the West. Approximately 10 million workers in Egypt earn (an average of) $500 per year. If no interest were charged, every cent earned by every Egyptian for seven years would be required to pay the debt. With interest included, it would require every cent earned by every Egyptian forever just to pay the interest. And what if every Egyptian does not contribute every cent earned?

3. The fact that repayment of these loans is close to impossible becomes more obvious every day. Former West German Chancellor Helmut Schmidt is proposing that "everyone face reality" and start "writing down" Third World debt.[23] At the same time, leading International Monetary Fund

experts are claiming that some major debts are worth 15 cents on the dollar. If that prospect is too grim, the only choice is to make more bad loans for as long as we can.

With the realization in mind that many countries are on the brink of default, President Reagan in November 1985 pleaded with reluctant bankers to approve $20 billion in new loans for needy Latin American nations (*U.S. News & World Report*, November 11, 1985). Another $9 billion was requested from the World Bank. Why this money is needed for loans may have been best expressed by Harold Evans, Editorial Director, *U.S. News & World Report*, as stated in his January 20, 1986, editorial:

> When governments are not repaid they can tax, borrow or print. Banks have a nasty habit of going broke. If the U.S. banks insisted tomorrow on all their hired money coming back on time, they wouldn't get it, and the world economy would start to come apart. A sudden default by Mexico, Brazil, Argentina and Venezuela could wipe out the capital of seven of the nine largest U.S. banks and two of four in Britain.
>
> That is a doomsday scenario. Let's make it more cheerful. If Argentina, Mexico and Brazil merely missed one year's payment, it would be a loss of $8 billion [to U.S. banks]. But add the wind-chill factor. To keep to the legal ratio of capital to loans, the banks would have to cut lending by about $160 billion. Money for jobs, homes, and businesses would freeze.

Perhaps another quotation by H. A. Hudlund, chairman of the board, Montezuma State Bank, sums it up best: "There are too few real bankers running too damn many banks. The situation is a hell of a mess—but you [the public] ain't seen nothing yet!"[24]

It should become apparent that it is not possible to extend help to other nations without having to pay the price here at home.

Take copper mining, for example: U.S. mining is being destroyed by cheap imports. U.S. copper production is down 75 percent since 1960. The United States is no longer a leading exporter and now imports a majority of the copper it requires. Copper mining is important as a source of jobs and corporate profits as well as for national security and for a positive balance of trade. Reagan refused when he was asked to help the survival of this multibillion dollar industry that was trapped with large debts fixed at an interest rate of 18 percent. He did so because the United States imports almost all of its copper from Chile, which has a $22-billion debt.

In fact, the United States, through the World Bank and the IMF, has recently lent hundreds of millions of additional dollars to Chile so that it can increase its copper exports. It is believed higher exports will enable Chile to raise enough money to make its debt payment. However, the United States is indirectly paying the Chilean debt anyway.

In the words of C. V. Myers, "Every debt will eventually be paid—if not by the borrower, then by the lender [when the borrower defaults]."[25]

If the above statement is not clear, consider the case of Poland. In 1982 Western banks extended Poland's 1982 debt for another 7-1/2 years with a 4-year grace period. Poland then requested its $25-billion debt to be extended another 20 years with the first 8 years as a grace period with no monies due. In 1982, 75 percent of the debt was rescheduled but with an interesting requirement: One-half of the $1.1-billion interest payment was to be made in trade as Polish steel products.[26]

At the same time LTV, America's third biggest steel producer, became the largest company ever to file bankruptcy, and second largest producer, Bethlehem Steel, posted another quarter of losses. Those losses totaled $2 billion, and American steelworkers were being laid off in droves. Yet American and Western banks agreed to accept $550 million worth of Polish nails per year. Thus, we trade American jobs for Polish jobs to help prevent the realization that nations are in default. It is extremely important to help them appear to be solvent, because if nations appear to be in default, the facade of our banking system will be exposed.*

The immediacy of the problem, however, can best be exemplified by a meeting held July 30, 1985, in Latin America. This meeting was hosted by Cuba's Fidel Castro to convince other South American nations to repudiate their (then) $360 billion debt. Cuba would, of course, take great pleasure in destroying the financial strength of the West, and America in particular. However, the other nations are not yet willing to kill the golden goose.

It is not that they have any loyalty to, or appreciation for, the nations that lent them so much (contempt is more likely). Nor do the borrowing nations feel it is their duty to pay their way. Instead, these nations are motivated by the need for more cash. The International Monetary Fund and the banks to which these nations owe so much money keep lending (giving) Third World nations more money (that they will never pay back) and extending the due dates of old loans so the debtor nations will keep playing the game and not openly declare default. The banks keep throwing money away because open default would collapse the banking system.

What would happen if the banking system collapsed? Depositors and borrowers would stand to lose everything. Bank loans would be called in, causing assets, businesses, and homes to be sold. But with no money to purchase them, for how much could they be sold?† If they were sold for a fraction of their worth, the debt could not be repaid. Businesses would find that they were "cash poor" and that sales would almost stop. Thus, there would be massive layoffs and a depression much worse than the one in 1929. Although people lost money in the 1929 depression, money in 1929 still had value. Certainly, today's government would not sit idly by; it would come to the rescue by printing hundreds of billions of dollars as fast as the presses could

---

*Protecting the facade becomes progressively more difficult. Additional loans were needed to prevent Polish default. Poland in 1989 has a $40-billion debt but is less likely than ever to pay it back.

†Some estimates have stated that the sale of assets during such a crisis would yield only 5 cents on the dollar.

run to put enough money in the banks so everyone could withdraw their share.

The only problem is that the money would be worthless. With no confidence in the financial system and with the presses rolling full steam, inflation would break all records. Consider some examples. Can you imagine a $20 meal costing $680 one year later? That is what happened in Bolivia with 3,400-percent inflation in 1985. That is equal to 1.5 percent per business day. In Bolivia a stack of bills many times bigger and heavier than a pack of cigarettes is needed to buy a pack of cigarettes.

Argentina has long been plagued with high inflation. In 1970 it was forced to issue new money with an exchange rate of 100 to 1. In 1983 inflation again made money so worthless that new currency had to be issued, this time with four zeros removed. Thus, 10,000 *"Peso Leys"* became 1 *"Peso Argentino"* overnight. In other words, a millionaire in 1970 would be broke if he bought a cup of coffee in 1983. Peru had 2,000 percent inflation in 1988, and Brazil started 1989 with inflation at 1,500 percent. This problem tends only to worsen. In these countries, checks must be written for 10 percent more than the goods purchased just to compensate for the lower value of the funds when they clear.

The United States is not the only country with a shaky banking system. Internationally, the problems would be severe, since all banking nations (developed nations) would be in a similar fix. But the country-to-country chaos would be insurmountable. Presently, international trade is conducted in U.S. dollars, and a great many of these dollars are floating around. The U.S. dollars held by other countries have very little backing other than faith in their stability. However, the dollar's lack of stability was demonstrated in September–October 1985, when the United States, Japan, France, England, and Germany dumped (sold) $10.2 billion on the world market and the dollar dropped 11.5 percent against other currencies by year's end and another 5 percent in the first two months of 1986.

The following year (1987) news of a record-setting U.S. trade deficit caused Japan, Germany, and Taiwan to print $70 billion of their own currencies to buy up dollars to stop its slide. What do you suppose they did with all those dollars? The foreign central banks used the dollars to buy U.S. Treasury Securities. Thus demonstrating the fallacy of creating yet another temporary band-aid. The dollar's slip was caused by mounting foreign debt, but the solution only further increased foreign debt. Like so much else in the banking industry "stability" was achieved with mirrors.

When the collapse comes, it will demonstrate that all paper is in itself worthless. Trade and international debts will have to be handled in barter or in bullion. Unfortunately, the annual U.S. trade deficit in 1986 was $168 billion. This is more than that of all other nations put together and large enough to bankrupt every nation in the world except America because of present faith in the dollar. But the bubble will have to burst.

The world's richest country is itself a debtor nation. Foreign assets in the United States overtook U.S. assets abroad in 1985, making America a debtor nation. To help finance its huge debt, the government has encouraged deposits in American banks from foreign sources. This necessary money was lured by high interest rates, low U.S. inflation, and confidence in the stability of the dollar. At latest count, foreigners held $340 billion of the U.S. debt. Of course, if inflation rose or the interest rate dropped relative to other nations, or if confidence in the dollar waned, this large foreign deposit would quickly disappear. How the government would obtain the money it needs without this source is unclear. What is clear is the size of the U.S. debt. The Federal Government owes $2.35 trillion which is equal to a stack of dollars 20 times greater than the diameter of the Earth.

When the collapse comes, there will be protectionism and trade restraints as never before. Everything will be COD,* in barter, or bullion. Where will trade-deficit nations get enough bullion? They will have to confiscate it from their citizens as the United States did in 1933.† Will the governments at least pay the citizens for the confiscated gold and silver? Do not bet on it. The

---

*To increase sales, Japan had liberal credit terms with trading partners. However, faced with $30 billion in bad foreign loans (credits), Japan is cutting trade with some countries.

†In the 1930s, not only could a citizen receive a 10-year prison term for possessing gold, but also a person could be sent to jail for saying that a bank was going to fail.

United States did not pay for the gold confiscated in 1933. If the U.S. Government did pay for the gold, it would be forced by law to pay the official recognized rate of $42.22 per ounce.* At the time of confiscation, however, gold would not be selling for its present value of $400 per ounce, but closer to $4,000 per ounce. Of course, the $42 payment would be in paper, which at the time might buy a pack of cigarettes.

On an international scale, the problems of the Third World countries may not really be the trigger to start this ball rolling. If Russia, with its significant economic difficulties, determines that it cannot out-race the United States in arms buildup because America has too much "wealth," then it might attempt to damage that wealth and gain support from the Third World nations it is trying to win over. Russia could claim that the Western banks caused the poverty in Third World nations through exploitation and high interest rates. Russia could then declare that the evil West should "forgive" its debtors and give aid rather than charge interest to these countries. The debtor nations would love this but would still need more cash. What if Russia promised (however insincerely) to give cash to debtor nations that repudiated debts to Western banks? Russia could declare that it would not make any debt payments to the West if the latter does not go along with the plan to help the needy nations. In so doing, the USSR would accomplish the following worldwide goals:

1. Create the image of a hero and win Third World friends.
2. Make the West look like victimizers.
3. Reduce its own debt payments and that of its satellites.
4. Cause economic collapse of its stronger archrival.

---

*The official U.S. value for gold (90 percent gold, 10 percent copper) was $20.67 per troy ounce until 1934, when its value was fixed at the famous $35.00 per ounce figure. On March 19, 1968, President Johnson removed gold backing of U.S. currency. On August 15, 1971, President Nixon announced that gold would no longer be used to settle international debts. On May 18, 1972, gold was revalued at $38.00 per ounce, and in February 1973, the dollar was devalued another 10 percent by fixing gold at $42.22 per ounce. On August 14, 1974, President Ford signed a law making it legal for citizens to own gold once again. This repealed a 41-year-old law enacted when the U.S. Government confiscated privately held gold in 1933.

By following such a strategy,* Russia would have everything to gain and nothing to lose. Russia may even be able to gain a strong foothold in many European nations, since unrest and economic weakness have always been major areas of successful takeovers for communism.

But it may be an opportunity for more than a communist takeover. Major crises are followed by radical political changes. A controlling international leader/government, which is unthinkable now, may become a necessity. International trade now makes up the majority of most gross national products. This may be setting the stage for what John and Nostradamus refer to as the Beast, or Antichrist world leader who will control all finances.

Remember that in Germany before World War II it took a wheelbarrow full of money to buy a loaf of bread. Problems like 18-million percent inflation and 55-percent unemployment caused the people of Germany to give full dictatorial powers to a wallpaper hanger (Hitler). When people become desperate and do not have enough to eat, they want radical changes and will follow anyone who makes desired promises.

- **Finances**—riches and power—are the key.
- **Automation/computerization** is the control.
- **Financial crisis** of overextended credit and valueless money might just be the vehicle of opportunity to usher in a new world order.

As demonstrated in the next chapter, additional circumstances are developing that can topple our teetering worldwide economic system. But beware! If John and Nostradamus are correct, you will not be willing to adopt a "wait and see" attitude about the new world order.

---

*Gorbachev has already started considering this option. On December 7, 1988, he told the U.N. General Assembly that the West needed to forgive the unfair debt burden of the Third World. The only obstacle stopping Gorbachev from dropping the other shoe is that, at the moment, the West is eager to extend to the Soviets and its satellites billions in addition loans.

IV. GLOBAL INSTABILITY:
Floods, Famines, and Earthquakes

The impending financial changes described in the last chapter are but a part of the major flux that characterizes the world today. Even less controllable and more devastating instabilities are manifested in the Earth itself. To develop an understanding for the mechanisms of the Earth, we need to examine some past events associated with floods, famines, and earthquakes.

THE GREAT FLOOD

It seems likely that just about everyone is aware of the Biblical account of "The Flood." In fact, Moslems and Buddhists, as well as almost all older religions, have legends about a Great Flood.* Even people who do not have roots in the Middle East, such as African tribes, Indians in South America, and Eskimos, have legends of an angry God who caused an Earth-wide flood. Scientific debate about whether there was a flood is ongoing, with some recent scientific evidence now supporting such a worldwide event. How can we know for sure that there was a Great Flood?

Was there enough water during the Flood to cover the entire Earth, including its mountains? Scientific evidence, in the form of water marks and stains at the very highest parts of the Earth, substantiates a flood. Across the Earth, many cities and villages were completely covered with mud during the same period. Evidence shows that tremendous erosion took place across mountain ranges worldwide, all dating back to the same approximate time (which is the limit of accuracy for such measurements).

---

*Approximately 80,000 publications in 72 languages mention a global flood.

Of course, those who believe in the Flood say, "Well, the Flood obviously did that." Those who do not believe in the Flood would like to find an alternative solution, but they have not as yet come up with one. One of the less publicized dilemmas that could shoot supporters of the Flood out of the water, so to speak, is that the amount of water on Earth cannot account for such an event. This is not a small detail. How can mountains 29,000 feet tall be totally submerged? If it were possible to combine all the atmospheric, glacial, and subterranean water, the oceans would rise only 100 to 200 feet. Where 28,800 feet of additional water could come from has always been a major dilemma.

If we do some calculations, we find that this enigma becomes more perplexing. According to Biblical accounts, the Flood was caused by 40 days and 40 nights of heavy rain. The Flood was to have covered all land on Earth. To cover Mt. Everest, which is 29,000 feet above sea level, the worldwide rain would have to average 29,000 feet of water over every square inch of the Earth. To accomplish this in 40 days, the water would have to rise at a fantastic rate: 960 feet per day, or more than 40 feet per hour, which is almost 500 inches per hour! That means the water rose by more than 8 inches every minute for 40 days and nights.

To envision how overwhelming 500 inches per hour (or 8 inches per minute) of rain is, compare this rate to a cloudburst in California, where 5 inches of rain fell in one hour and washed buildings away. A home garden hose with the faucet turned wide open would fill a 55-gallon drum at approximately 8 inches per minute. Is there a scientific explanation that can account for such a downpour? And where did all this water come from? To understand what may have contributed to the answer, we need to examine the Earth and the space it occupies.

COSMOS

Did you know that you are the remains of a dead star? Consider the formation of the universe.

Scientists are in almost total agreement that our universe was created by a colossal explosion called the Big Bang. For reasons unknown, all of the existing matter and antimatter simultaneously combined to create large quantities of the simplest atom, hydrogen (consisting of only one proton and one electron). The Big Bang explosion also created enough energy to scatter this newly made hydrogen throughout the universe.

As this gas drifted through the cosmos, gravitational forces slowly caused the formation of large clouds. Once a cloud started to form, its gravity would increase as its mass grew, thus ensuring that it would collect more gas and would continue to grow. Because all of this gas was moving at great speed, some of the motion would be transformed into rotation about its center of gravity. As the mass grew, the gas would be more compressed, and the rotational speed would increase. (Think of an ice skater pulling in her arms during a spin.)

The cloud would continue to gather gas, causing it to become more dense and its rotational speed to increase. This may continue for millions or perhaps billions of years. Two limiting factors would prevent this growth from continuing indefinitely.

First, as the outer edge of the spinning cloud approached a speed too energetic for the gravitational field to contain, matter would break away or be thrown out. This matter might end up orbiting around the mother cloud as a separate body. As mass was ejected, the main cloud would lose some rotational speed.* The amount of material ejected would be determined by the mass and speed of the cloud as well as the type of matter within the cloud. In the early universe, the only material available to be ejected was hydrogen.

Second, as the gas was compressed by the growing gravitational field, the pressure and temperature of the cloud would increase until a thermonuclear reaction was triggered. In a thermonuclear reaction, energetic atoms are fused together to form heavier

---

*If an ice skater were spinning with a brick in her hand and she let the brick go, it would be thrust out as if it had been thrown. The effect on the skater would be a push in the opposite direction, thus slowing her down. Letting go is the same thing as throwing because the force is still in the brick. Like the skater, the cloud was slowed down by the material thrown out.

atoms. The fusion process releases great quantities of energy, which heat the gas and cause it to expand. When the fusion reaction is triggered (by critical mass), a star is born.

Every star exists as a balance between the collapsing force of gravity and the explosive force of the fusion reaction. Since nothing lasts forever, the star would eventually (after millions or billions of years) use up all of its hydrogen, having converted it all to the second lightest element, helium. As this occurred, its nuclear explosions would start to die out, and the star would again collapse. Because of this collapse, temperatures and pressures would again increase until a more energetic fusion reaction took place. In this fusion reaction, helium would be converted to carbon, again giving off large amounts of energy for millions of years. When all of the helium had been converted to carbon, the cycle of using up fuel, collapsing, and then starting a new fusion reaction would continue. The star, which was ever smaller and more energetic, would next make oxygen, then silicon, and finally iron. However, the cycle would stop because no simple fusion step can turn iron into a heavier element.

As a star uses up all of its silicon fuel, it begins to cool and collapse, and this collapse, in turn, creates enormous pressure. For many stars, using all of the silicon fuel and collapsing is the last phase. But for stars that are more than eight times larger than our sun (some stars are millions of times more massive), the pressures become so enormous that one last great reaction takes place: a supernova. This cataclysmic explosion releases more energy than the star releases in all its former life; it releases more energy, in fact, than entire galaxies containing billions of stars. The supernova explosion is powerful enough to create every known element (and perhaps some that are still unknown). The force of this final explosion destroys the star, throwing its newly made heavy material throughout the cosmos at speeds that exceed 6,000 miles per second in a spectacle that is visible for hundreds of years (see Figure IV-1).

Figure IV-1. The Supernova

The Orion Nebula seen as the central star in Orion's sword is the remnant of a supernova. For the first second of the explosion, the supernova releases more energy than the entire universe. Energy output is equal to 10 million stars for many years following the explosion.

As this heavy matter travels through space it may eventually become part of some newly forming gas cloud. If this new cloud grows large enough, it could repeat the whole process. It, too, would be mostly hydrogen gas subjected to centrifugal forces. As this younger cloud continued to compress, its rate of rotation would increase. Eventually, it could be required to eject some material, which eventually could solidify into orbiting planets.[*] Thus, everything that exists on Earth (including people) that is not

---

[*]Although theories vary as to how these planets were formed, they do not disagree about the results. Thus, their disagreement does not affect this discussion.

hydrogen (gas) is by necessity part of a long-dead, distant star that was destroyed in a supernova. If the Earth had not been formed from a second, third, or fifteenth generation star (our sun), we would not be here because our planet would be just hydrogen.

Some years ago, it was recognized that the planets follow a geometric progression. From the orbits of Mercury, Venus, Earth, Mars, Jupiter, and Saturn, the orbits of Neptune, and Uranus could be predicted. The relationships are based on the natural progression that the planets follow because of the way in which they were formed. However, following this geometric progression would lead to prediction of a planet-like body orbiting the sun between Mars and Jupiter. Such a body does not exist. Instead, this orbit is occupied by the asteroid belt. Long before the familiar comic strip character was created, scientists named the planet believed to have broken up into these asteroids: Krypton.

Other scientists found that they could predict the density (not the overall mass) of the planets and what they are made of by knowing their orbits. The inner bodies are called the heavy planets, and the outer ones (those past Mars) are called the lighter planets. The latter, made up mostly of methane and other frozen gases, are extremely light for their size. The heavy planets are made of rock and metal. Knowing the density of the Earth and calculating when it had been thrown out and how much momentum would have been given up by its release, one could predict what kind of material had to have been thrown out to create the other planets. It was predicted that the other inner planets would have to be made up basically of iron and nickel, which is what constitutes the Earth's core. The Earth basically should not have much water on it—certainly not oceans. Thus, the question of where much of the Earth's water came from appears unanswerable unless we examine areas outside the Earth itself. One such source, which makes daily contact with the Earth, is meteors.

Museums exhibit meteorites, which resemble black pitted iron or stone chunks. However, these stony meteorites represent only a small portion of the 600 meteors per minute that crash into the Earth's atmosphere. The vast majority of the meteorites coming from the frozen depths of space are actually solid water. Because

Krypton's orbit is farther from the sun than the heavy planets but closer than the lighter gaseous planets, most of Krypton would have to be made up of material somewhere in between these two extremes. Density calculations of Krypton indicate that it is made up mainly of water, like most meteors.

Noah supposedly knew 120 years in advance that the Flood would come. Is it possible that a Celestial Being could have purposely altered the direction of some orbiting meteors in space hundreds or thousands of years before that climatic event? Could a minor change in speed or direction push objects far enough off course after 120 years to cause a collision with some other body such as Earth? If course corrections are made far enough in advance, they do not require much effort. For example, consider the ease of reversing the direction of a high speed auto on a superhighway over a wide bend in 60 seconds compared with the impossible task of accomplishing the same result in 1 second. This line of reasoning is not an attempt to discount divine abilities but, rather, to ask what are the scientific possibilities concerning where the Earth came from, what we are made up of, how were these planets thrown out in space, and what do they consist of? Does the Earth possess the amount of water that scientists would predict? If not, where could so much extra water come from?

In the early formation of the planets, a lot of space debris hit the Earth and contributed material it would not otherwise have had. The light "floating continents" and the seas themselves are to a large extent the result of this interplanetary transfer. The explanation for many earthly phenomena lies beyond the planet itself in cosmic relationships. For example, it is possible that the Flood was caused by a fantastic 40 day and night meteor shower that inundated the Earth with 8 inches of falling water per minute. No normal rainstorm could do that, especially since it would have to be worldwide. A meteor shower of ice may be one of the only ways to affect the whole Earth simultaneously.

If the Earth went through such a cataclysmic event, could other planets completely escape the effects? Probably not. When the United States placed its Viking spacecraft in orbit around Mars and later landed Mariner on the surface to analyze its atmosphere, topography, and soil, virtually no water was found. However, it was evident that Mars once had water because the photos show the remnants of ancient lakes that were 3 miles deep and larger than Lake Superior. The planet also shows signs of great water erosion and of flood plains across its surface (see Figure IV-2). Imagine floods on a planet that now has no water. Could the flood on Mars be connected with the Great Flood on Earth? If a meteor shower explains the origin of the Flood, then where did all that water go?

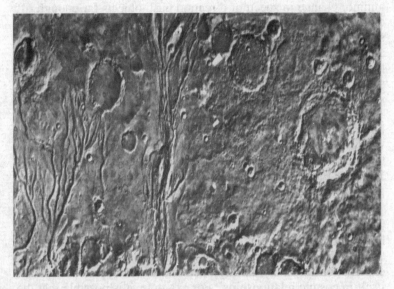

Figure IV-2. Water on Mars

This photo taken by the Viking spacecraft clearly shows the remnants of an ancient flood plain and river network on the surface of Mars.

The answer may lie with the solar wind, a stream of subatomic particles that are continuously blown off the surface of the sun. The Earth is continuously radiated by ultraviolet light, which causes the breakup of water into hydrogen and oxygen. These light elements are produced at the very surface of the highest ionosphere of the Earth and are blown away by the 1 million mph solar wind. The solar wind constantly blows and pushes against the atmosphere of the Earth. Presently, we lose about 50 million tons of water a day to the solar wind. In ancient times the moisture content of the Earth may have been higher, the Earth's temperature may have been different, or the solar wind may have been stronger. Could the Earth have lost most of the water that caused the Flood? It is possible. The point to remember here is that explaining the Flood illustrates the Earth's close relationship to the cosmos.

EARTHQUAKES

If the Flood was an ancient disaster, consider a modern type of devastation—earthquakes. Some people claim that more earthquakes are measured today than a few years ago because more equipment is available to detect them. However, just a couple of seismographs throughout the world can tell us where all the earthquakes are located and how much energy was released (their rating). Between 1897 and 1946, earthquakes registering six or more on the Richter Scale occurred at the rate of three every 10 years. Between 1946 and 1956, the rate was seven; between 1956 and 1966, the rate grew to 17; by the 1967 to 1976 period, the number of large earthquakes had swelled to 180. That is an increase of 6,000 percent in only 40 years. Look at Mt. St. Helens blowing smoke, soot, and steam into the atmosphere. It is also happening in Mexico, Alaska, Italy, Japan, Columbia, and Hawaii.

Except for isolated disasters, the Earth has been gentle, quiet, and consistent. The Earth has been so consistent lately that it is taken for granted. In fact, the scientific community set a standard, called the solar standard, that states that the sun never changes and, therefore, can be used as a constant energy source by which to measure many things. However, within the last 10 years, satellite studies of the sun found that the sun's energy varies, albeit only a fraction of a percent per year. The long-term variation is unknown because these satellites are relatively new. But one thing is clear: The sun does vary, and there is no solar constant. This variation could not be measured from Earth because of all the clould interference and weather patterns. Sun spots, which actually alter the amount of heat leaving the sun, indicate cycles of change and cause changes in the solar wind and the weather patterns on Earth. But the energy of the sun itself, which takes 22 years to move from its center to its surface because of its enormous size, was thought to be unchangeable.

Recently, we have begun to understand the sun-Earth relationship better. We now know why in 1979 Sky Lab fell from space prematurely. This space lab, which ironically was created to study the sun, was destroyed by the sun itself. The sun experienced a temporary increase in its energy output, which heated the Earth's upper atmosphere, causing it to expand. The result was additional drag on Sky Lab, slowing it down and causing it to crash to the Earth.* Thus, the sun's inconsistencies are not insignificant. We have also learned that sun spots affect the sun's radiation. For example, between 1645 and 1755 virtually no sun spots were observed, and the world experienced uncommonly cold weather. Rivers in Europe reportedly froze that have not been known to freeze since. Sun spots also affect the charged particles of the solar wind that cause the eerie glow of the northern lights as well as the amount of charged particles in our atmosphere. This, in turn, affects radio communications and global rainfall.

The relationship of sun spots to rainfall has recently been established by studies made of solidified algae-rich mud layers. By examining the layers of dark summertime mud and lighter solidified winter mud in Australian lake beds, scientists have been able to read (like tree rings) the rainfall pattern for hundreds and thousands of years of Earth's past. The results show that the rain pattern on Earth follows the sun's cycle of spots.

The sun is not constant, and neither is the Earth. It had been thought there was nothing more stable than solid ground, but we now know that the continents are floating and traveling across the

---

*Ten years later we are still learning our lesson. The peaking of the sun's 22–year sun spot cycle (peaking occurs twice each cycle) has caused further expansion of the Earth's atmosphere. As a result the satellite to study the sun, Solar Max, was also dragged down by friction and destroyed in December 1989.

planet. If we traced all the continental movements back in time, we would find that they are all parts of a single super-continent called Pangaea. Because of continental drift, this super-continent broke up and became all of the major land masses and continents on Earth, the center of which is now known as Antarctica. Antarctica is Earth's highest* and most mineral-rich continent. This is significant because Antarctica may have been the center of a large body that collided with Earth in its infancy. This is evident because the continents are floating over the heavy basalt, which makes up the ocean basins.[†] Antarctica is the only continent on Earth that man has not destroyed or molested because it is covered by 6,500 feet of ice.

Geologists claim that things happen on Earth gradually and that major changes take tens of thousands of years. Common belief is that mountains grow at a centimeter a year and that they weather away at about the same rate and thus stay about the same size. Actually, that explanation is extremely unlikely. Although mountains may have started doing things millions of years ago, every once in a while they hiccup, burp, and grow, causing changes that are not measured by centimeters.

The 1964 earthquake in Alaska lasted 30 seconds and registered about 8.3 on the Richter Scale. This quake surprised scientists because it destroyed buildings that were thought to be earthquake proof and produced a *tsunami* or tidal wave[‡] hundreds of feet in height. That *tsunami* completely annihilated the city it hit. The city of Valdez has been reconstructed 8 miles from its original site to prevent that from happening again. This *tsunami* did something that was thought to be impossible. It was clocked by jet to have exceeded 450 miles per hour as it went all the way to Antarctica.

---

*Antarctica's mean land elevation is 6,004 feet. This is much higher than any other continent.

[†]Not only is the basalt chemically different from continental crust, but recent studies have shown that continental rocks are significantly older than the rocks of the ocean basins that make up the vast majority of the Earth's crust.

[‡]The term tidal wave is commonly, but erroneously, applied to large waves generated by submarine earthquakes.

While cruising on Prince William Sound in Alaska, one can look toward the ocean side and see that all of the trees are bare, dead skeletons. The reason is that when the earthquake hit, that whole vast area sank 6 feet and allowed saltwater to reach the tree roots. This was not the case on the other side of the bay, where the whole mountain range rose 65 feet and created high cliffs. That 65–foot movement took only 30 seconds. That is how mountain ranges are made.[*]

A lot of geological changes happen because of a continual buildup of force to the point where something gives. The "give" can be an earthquake, volcanic action, or similar readjustments that make and/or destroy things quickly, not in tens and thousands of years. A 65–foot rise every couple of thousand years could after a million years create the largest mountain on Earth, and less frequent or smaller movements could result in smaller ranges.

The ability of Earth movements to destroy cities and to take human life has been recognized since the beginning of history. Consider, for example, some events in the distant past:

Location	Date	Deaths
Mount Vesuvius, Italy	79	20,000
Mount Etna, Sicily	1669	20,000
Lisbon, Portugal (*tsunami*)	1755	60,000
Mount Krakatoa, Indonesia	1883	36,000
Mount Pelée, Martinque	1902	30,000
Sicily, Italy (earthquake)	1908	76,000
Central Italy (earthquake)	1915	30,000
Kansu, China (earthquake)	1920	200,000
Tokyo, Japan (earthquake)	1923	160,000
Quetta, India (earthquake)	1935	30,000
Concepción, Chile (earthquake)	1939	25,000

[*]Alaskan mountain growth is not an isolated case. In 1538, near the Italian city of Pozzoli, a mountain range grew 400 feet in three days. Upliftings of as much as 10,000 feet have occurred in the wake of retreating ice sheets.

All sites listed are still active and capable of creating equal or greater destruction at any time.

In the last 80 years, earthquakes and the resulting floods have destroyed the capital city of Managua, Nicaragua, four times, with loss of life reported in the tens of thousands. Ecuador in 1949 had an earthquake that killed 5,000. Peru in 1970 had earthquakes that each took over 50,000 lives. A 1976 quake in Guatemala also claimed 23,000 lives. The greatest loss of life occurred on July 28, 1976, in Tangshan, China, where a magnitude 8 earthquake collapsed a city with an area the size of San Francisco and took 750,000 lives. It certainly seems that the so-called solid Earth is not stable.

More recently, three disasters in 1985 took tens of thousands of lives:

Location	Event	Month (1985)	Deaths
Bangladesh	Tidal wave	May	10,000
Mexico	Earthquake	September	7,000
Columbia	Volcano	November	25,000

Although every major earthquake does not take over 7,000 lives, the probability that cities will experience excessive damage and loss of life is demonstrated by the December 1988 quake in Soviet Armenia that took 25,000 lives. The trend is clear, major seismic events are occurring at an ever-increasing rate and the Earth, it would appear, is teetering on the edge of a delicate balance. How long can such a balance be maintained?

ENVIRONMENT

The weather has also been predictable in recent times. Its stability is fortunate because the weather greatly affects the world's population. The U.S. Department of Agriculture had stated for years that we keep producing more and more food because of better technology, irrigation, and farm equipment. To a large extent, some of that was true: Improvements made more land arable and have increased labor efficiency. However, since 1960 the Department of Agriculture has not made that claim because the actual production per acre has, on the average, decreased. Technological advances reached a plateau. Furthermore, the dominant reason for production increases was that the weather was unusually good: the right amount of rain, not too much insect infestation, not too much undesired heat, and little unexpected frost.

Unfortunately, the weather has ceased being mild and has started reverting back to less hospitable conditions. Daily weather reports tell us of record highs and lows within our nation. Climatologists have stated that eight of the last 10 years have been decisively abnormal. Alaska had spring in January, Phoenix had a "100 year flood" three times in 5 years. Florida citrus fruits froze 3 years in a row. The USSR has had crop failures for many years running. Drought in 1984 took 30 percent of U.S. corn production, to say nothing of the 5-year drought in Africa or the typhoon that killed 10,000 people in Pakistan.

Nature aside, in America we have mismanaged our water so that there is not enough to fill up our dams. We budgeted to use more water than falls from the sky and therefore cannot help but run out of this all-important life-giving resource. Do you realize that the Colorado River does not flow to the ocean anymore? America had to construct desalinization plants for the Mexicans because of guarantees made in treaties that promised Mexico water from the Colorado River. Water from the Mississippi River cannot be safely consumed because of the sewage and carcinogens continually dumped into this vital water resource.

We have created plagues by poisoning and depleting our ground water supply. We thought there was a lot of water in the ground that had been there for millions and millions of years. That may have been true, but in some cases, we took it out in 20 years. Corn cannot be grown in parts of Texas any longer because it takes too much water. The subterranean water tables have dropped hundreds of feet, leaving only a couple of feet to meet all vital needs for eons to come. When that is depleted, Texans will not be able to grow anything; so they have to conserve their water severely. This has not happened yet in Nebraska, which has the deeper portions of the Ogallala Aquifer, but that state may develop the same problem for the same reason as Texas.

In Southern California whole counties are sinking because, as water is pumped out of the ground, large voids are formed that cannot support the weight above it. Then the land itself fills in the void. When this happens, not only does the topography change, but also the ability to trap and store water is lost forever. One of the best documented cases is in San Jose, California where 125 square miles of the city and surrounding area has subsided 13 feet.[27] This has also happened in Florida, which has developed many large sink holes. Certainly, our toxic chemical spills may have depleted one of America's most fantastic natural resources.

Depletion of our water resource is overshadowed by the mismanagement and destruction of our drinking water. Many people are forced to buy bottled water to try to maintain reasonable health. The U.S. Government has earmarked $6 billion for a cleanup super fund to "fix" the worst chemical dump sites before they become more "Love Canals"* that could cause incalculable health problems and costly community evacuations. However, the cleanups have not yet been effective,† and new poison zones are discovered daily. The problem areas now number 2,565 out of the 175,000 known waste-disposal sites. But dangers extend beyond the known dump sites. Most contaminating chemicals are stored in 1.5–million underground steel tanks, 35 percent of which presently leak. What to do about chemical storage facilities and the 250 million tons of hazardous waste produced each year (2,000 lbs. per year for every resident) has become a burning national question.

---

*"Love Canal" is the name given a residential area in a section of Niagara Falls, New York, that was built over a legal dump site. After many people became sick and developed cancer from escaping ground gases, the state quarantined the area, and 2,000 residents were forced to move out of their homes permanently.

†In the first five years of the super fund program, 565 sites "of high priority" have been identified with 2,000 more sites known to be endangering public health. After spending $1.5 billion, six sites have been worked on, and zero sites are clean.

The Wall Street Journal reported on August 12, 1980, that TCE (Trichloroethylene), a widely used carcinogen, has reached deep aquifers that supply half of America's water supply.* How much death and disease will be caused by chemical dumping and pollution is unknown. At least 63 percent of America's water supply is unsafe for consumption and, to date, 2,100 foreign substances in our water supply have been identified. The problem will continue to worsen because chemicals dumped a quarter of a century ago are only now entering the water systems. The next decade or two may leave us little potable water.

With respect to water, weather, and a delicate balance, consider *El Niño*, which is a slight 3 mph wind that lasts up to three years. What possible consequence can such a small wind have? Unfortunately, because of the delicate balance of the Earth, the consequences are substantial. The breeze of *El Niño* in 1982–1983 caused water in the western Pacific Ocean to move eastward to the Americas. This extra water caused tides to be substantially above normal, resulting in major flooding and property damage, including many buildings washed into the sea.

This water movement also changed the sea current and, coupled with the warm wind, caused the ocean (especially along the continents) to warm by several degrees. Although it was only 2 to 3 degrees higher, the water was too warm (91°F) for plankton to live. Without plankton, small fish died and washed up on the shore by the trillions. Of course, without small fish, large fish cannot survive. Peruvian fishing boats often did not leave port for the last two years of *El Niño*. Many fishermen were forced to become shrimpers as the anchovetas and sardines all but disappeared in an area that had been called the fishing capital of the world.[28]

---

*The cost to everyone concerned for past mistakes was demonstrated in San Jose, California. A chemical spill by IBM has already cost the company $25 million in cleanup activities and $20 million in preventive improvements. Still, Ted Smith of the Silicon Valley Toxics Coalition, stated in February 1986, "an awful lot more needs to be done by IBM." What do they do with the 417 million gallons a day of contaminated water that is pumped from the ground? They dump it in overland streams that lead to vital aquifers and ultimately to San Francisco Bay.

This gentle, warm breeze had still another effect. Its warm air allowed for improved evaporation over the Pacific. The moisture-laden air drenched North and South America with record rainfalls that flooded vast areas and washed homes down mountainsides in rivers of mud (see Figure IV-3). In July 1983, 400,000 Brazilians were left homeless because of the relentless precipitation. This wind was felt worldwide and played a part in the African drought which claimed millions of lives. As demonstrated by *El Niño*, even small and seemingly insignificant events can have overwhelming and far-reaching effects on this planet's ability to support life.

Figure IV-3. Effects of *El Niño*

Two of the homes at the top are overhanging the ridge. A total of seven homes were destroyed at this site in Oakland, California. The abnormally high rainfall amounted to 30 inches for the year, about the same as is normal for New York. Thus, change more than quantity can have major consequences.

El Niño is not the only cause for abnormal rainfall. After *El Niño* ended in 1983, the midwestern United States experienced excessive rainfall while the southeast had its worst drought on record. As the southeast started water rationing after four years of below–average rainfall, Chicago and Salt Lake City faced flooding. Once thought to be stable, the Great Salt Lake has risen 12.5 feet, flooding the resort of Saltair, submerging Interstate 80, and causing a threat to Salt Lake City (see Figure IV-4). Taxpayers paid for three multimillion dollar pumps to help control the lake level. So much water has entered the lake that its salinity decreased from 23 to 5.5 percent as the lake expanded by 700 square miles.

Figure IV-4. Record-Setting Rise in the Great Salt Lake

The pictures above illustrate how systems thought to be stable may change. The time between photographs was 3 years.

Downtown Chicago faced similar flooding problems because the Great Lakes had risen 10 feet in three years. Because of their size (the lakes contain enough water to cover the entire nation with 10 feet of water), no engineering plan is feasible. Thus, man must learn that he cannot always alter his environment at will.

However, without willing it, man may cause an adverse affect on the environment as pollution and industrial by-products continue to accumulate (see Figure IV-5).

Figure IV-5. Effects of Polluted Air

Not long ago, children were sent outside for healthy fresh air. The rash on this Mexico City boy's face was caused by air pollution. Although air pollution claims 400 lives a month in Mexico City, the impending worldwide health problems caused by destruction of the ozone layer will pose a much larger threat.

Some seemingly small buildups of pollution appear to have almost no impact at all—for awhile. Then suddenly the ecological system "snaps," and irreversible damage is observed. This is the case with acid rain. Since the Industrial Revolution, smokestack industries have dumped their waste (pollution) into the life-supporting envelope of air that surrounds our planet. People used to believe that the atmosphere of the Earth was essentially infinite and that eventually the soot and ash in the air would be "washed out" by rain. What was not realized was that the sulfur in this smoke mixes with atmospheric moisture to create sulfurous acid, which then precipitates as _acid rain_. Acid rain was always known to be potentially harmful, but what was to be done? There was no "hard evidence" that acid rain would do any real harm. In addition, trying to identify acid rain sources hundreds or thousands of miles away across political boundaries compounded the problem.

Research has continued, and the most startling observation was made in Canada while studying a naturally occurring coal fire that has been smoldering for hundreds of years. This subterranean fire, which cannot be put out, and its associated smoke and acid rain killed all life in the lakes within a 25-mile radius. The surprise was that within a mile or two of this circle, lakes were found to be almost completely normal with healthy life forms. It was concluded that natural buffers (minerals or microorganisms) neutralized the acid until the buffers were either used up or destroyed. When the natural buffers were overwhelmed, the lakes quickly turned acid, and all life died. Thus, the effect of acid rain is usually observed not as gradual, but more often as a sudden, irreversible tragedy.*

Today acid rain is a serious international problem. New York's Adirondack Mountains have 200 "dead" lakes, eastern Canada has 4,600 lakes that cannot support life, and Sweden has 9,000 lakes that are "dead" or are feared to be "dying." In addition, extensive forest losses have been reported in Poland, East Germany, and the Soviet Union. West Germany claims one-third of its trees may be killed, while Czechoslovakia states that 10 percent of its trees have already been destroyed. Since the sources of acid rain pollution are not likely to "go away," one can only wonder what new areas will be affected and how quickly they will "snap" out of their life-supporting role.

Sometimes man's disregard and/or ignorance can result in redefinition of the quality of life on Earth. For example, consider the case of air conditioning. Air conditioning is a commonplace luxury today that we tend to take for granted. But commercial air conditioning actually got a slow start. Refrigeration works on the principle that a hot gas cools as it expands. A refrigerator (or freezer) requires a gas that will liquefy during the compression cycle and expand as much as possible during the cooling cycle.

---

*Efforts in upstate New York to neutralize an acid lake by placing tons of antacid in the water have been of little value.

The efficiency of the refrigerator depends on the expansion properties of the gas and the ability of the gas to absorb heat (specific heat). Since few gases would liquefy at the necessary temperature, early refrigerators used ammonia even though it is corrosive and poisonous.

Refrigeration was destined to have formidable obstacles until Du Pont developed a replacement for ammonia that was nontoxic, noncorrosive, and characterized by the desired properties of high expansion and specific heat. Production of this gas requires substitution of chlorine and fluorine for the hydrogen in simple hydrocarbons (i.e., methane and butane). The new substance was considered a miracle chemical because it not only made refrigeration and air conditioning practical, but also found many other uses. Because it is non-carcinogenic, nonflammable, and able to dissolve fats, this new substance was used as an industrial degreaser and an all purpose cleaner. It is used in fire extinguishers and in plasma etching to manufacture chips for the semiconductor industry. Its expansion qualities and inertness made it a natural propellant with the invention of the spray can.

This miracle gas has become known worldwide as Freon™*. In the mid-1970s, this heavy Freon gas was recognized as a potential threat: It could enter the upper atmosphere and destroy the ozone layer. As a result, the United States passed a law in 1978 against the use of Freon as a propellant. U.S. lawmakers thought that they finally showed an environmental problem could be identified and corrected. But was it?

Ozone is produced and located in the ozonosphere some 100,000 feet above the Earth. The air at this altitude is very thin. At this altitude, energetic ultraviolet radiation from the sun reacts with the outer oxygen molecules to produce the unstable and short-lived ozone molecule. Unlike oxygen and air, ozone is opaque to UV and thus screens out almost all ultraviolet radiation![†] Without

---

*Freon is a trademark of the E. I. Du Pont De Nemours & Company.

[†]This ozone layer, however, is very thin, having the equivalent thickness of a dime (1/10 inch), if measured at standard temperature and pressure, i.e., 68°F and sea level.

ozone, the Earth would receive 330,000 percent more radiation. Under such conditions, every 10 seconds of exposure to the sky during the day would produce a burn equal to 9-1/2 hours of present sunlight. Thus, this thin, unstable layer of gas protects all life on Earth; without ozone, no plant could survive, and people would have to cover their skin and eyes completely during all daylight hours.

That would be the worst possible case. In a much less severe case, the Earth may lose only 1 to 5 percent of the ozone layer (at first). It is reported that a 1 percent decrease in ozone would cause 20,000 additional cases of skin cancer a year in the United States, and a 5 percent loss in ozone would increase ultraviolet radiation by 50 percent. This would kill many forms of aquatic plants, which are key to the food chain, while causing major increases in cataracts and skin cancer and a deficiency in the body's immune system (as does AIDS).[29]

Now that Freon has been outlawed, is there still cause for concern? Yes! Although the United States passed laws against the use of Freon as a propellant,* almost every other country still uses it.[†] Even U.S. consumption continues; in fact, its use has actually risen. Today, virtually all business offices, shopping centers, and stores, as well as the majority of new cars, have air conditioning. These air conditioning units use Freon. The Freon in all the many millions of existing air conditioners will likely leak out to the atmosphere over the next 5 to 10 years. In addition, Freon is still used in fire extinguishers, semiconductor manufacturing, and industrial solvents and cleaners.[‡] Even

---

*The aerosol can industry never really needed Freon as a propellant in the first place, since compressed air or nitrogen can be substituted. Therefore, it was relatively easy to pass a law against its use in the United States. Since other industries cannot easily find substitutes for Freon, big business will lobby hard and long against any restrictive legislative measure.

†Freon is sold and manufactured under various names by many companies throughout the world under license from E. I. Du Pont De Nemours & Company.

‡CBS reported on April 20, 1989 that a single IBM plant in San Jose California, releases to the atmoshpere 1.5 million pounds of Freon 13B-1 ($CBrF_3$) per year along with other Freon solvents. When asked by concerned citizens to switch to other less Earth destroying solvents an IBM spokesmen stated, "We can't. There is no substitute."

StyroFoam cups and insulation use Freon. Industrial use of Freon requires bottles that hold 100 to 10,000 pounds of gas, and these bottles are used at the rate of tens of thousands per year.

Satellite studies have shown that for the last three years a huge hole the size of the United States has formed in the ozone layer above the South Pole during the Antarctic spring and summer. A smaller hole has also started forming over the North Pole. This unnatural occurrence has also caused a decrease in ozone over Switzerland and other higher latitudes. This problem may be only the tip of the iceberg because Freon has been widely used for only 20 to 30 years, with the greatest use in the last 10 years. This heavy gas takes 10 to 100 years to reach the high altitudes of the ozonosphere. Therefore, if all manufacturing of Freon stopped today, the ozone problem would continue to increase until the twenty-second century. Thus, the wisdom that enabled science to produce this miracle gas may help us to understand the writings of John the Apostle: "…and a sore and grievous wound was made upon the men…and every live thing in the sea died. …The sun…was allowed to scorch mankind…" (Rev. 16: 2–9).

Other technical advances affect our ability to produce enough food. Technical advances appear to have realized their zenith and now seem to be counter-productive. Central California's San Joaquin Valley was the richest and most fertile farming area in the world. This valley is partly why two-thirds of America's fresh produce is grown in California.* Without irrigation, this valley could produce two bountiful crops per year, with no crops being grown in the hot, arid summer. However, with advances in irrigation, aqueducts were built to transport river water hundreds of miles to allow the valley to produce three crops per year. For a while production greatly increased. But the rivers transport salt from the mountains to the sea. They are now bringing that salt to the fertile farm land. Salt deposits are so obvious now in the San Joaquin Valley that a white crust can be seen covering the land. This has taken its toll on the productivity of the area as crop size

---

*This statement, made by the California Chamber of Commerce, is not intended to include grains (e.g., wheat, oats, corn) or stored crops such as potatoes.

is stunted and fewer types of crops can be grown. As a result, the most fertile valley in the world produces less now with three crops per year than it did with two crops per year, and it may soon produce no crops at all.

In Egypt the High Aswan Dam was built in 1970 to prevent floods and to provide water for Egypt's vast desert areas. The vast increases in productivity were not realized, however, because the rich farm land on the flood banks of the Nile, upstream from the dam, are now under 137 million acre feet of water. Downstream from the dam nutrient-rich flood waters no longer replenish the land. Although more land is available for planting, the desert has proved that irrigating poor soil produces poor harvests. This loss of nutrients has also caused the loss of the rich fisheries at the mouth of the Nile. Some Egyptians have suggested removal of the dam, but so much money has been spent on this great structure that its continued use seems certain.

Insect infestation is also taking its toll. In the warm stagnant waters behind dams, such as the High Aswan, insect populations and disease have skyrocketed. Even in the United States, the insect problem has gotten steadily worse. The U.S. Department of Agriculture claims that one-third of all seeds planted are consumed before they sprout, and one-third of all produce grown is lost to bugs. This loss causes farmers to use more insecticides. This increased usage may compound the problems of cost, water pollution, and food pollution. In 1985 millions of melons were removed from stores when they were found to contain so much insecticide as to cause serious illness or death.

Ironically, insecticides may cause the insect overpopulation. When bug poisons are first used, they reduce the population of the undesired insects, but they cannot eliminate all of them. (Their greatest effectiveness was from their introduction in the mid-1940s until the late 1950s.) The bugs that do survive are more resistant to the poisons, and they pass that trait on to their millions of offspring. Within a few generations and sprayings, a super-bug is produced that requires many times more poison to kill. The result is that it now costs as much as 2,000 times more to use insecticides than in the 1950s, and the effects are only marginal. Some poisons used today require sprayed fields to be quarantined for days after being treated. Some insecticides toxic to humans can cause death if absorbed through the skin. But a fly must ingest proportionately the equivalent of a pound of that same poison to be killed.*

As increased doses of insecticide are used, more life forms up the food chain consume increased amounts of tainted bugs, and are unintentionally killed. Then the insect problem worsens as the "good" bugs, such as wasps, ladybugs, and spiders, and some higher life forms, such as insect-eating bats and birds, succumb and even more crops are lost.

The long-term solution, of course, is to cut back substantially on insecticides and to let the natural predators become reestablished (either naturally or by scientifically encouraged means). But how many farmers are willing to give up insecticides, and thus production, for the years it would take to reestablish the natural balance? Meanwhile, the problem keeps getting worse. Several nations, including Russia, refused U.S. grain shipments in 1985 because they were infested with bugs. The response from the U.S. Department of Agriculture was less than reassuring. It claimed that the large number of bugs in U.S. wheat is now normal and that the bugs could be killed by chemically treating the stored wheat. Russia refused and so should everyone else. Who would want dead bugs ground into flour, and who needs one more poison added to food?†

Food production increased rapidly in the 1940s, 1950s, and early 1960s for reasons that until now concerned few scientists. The productivity per acre of corn, for instance, increased several times. This was accomplished by continually cross-breeding the

---

*At least 53 of the 300 pesticides used on food crops are carcinogenic. Half a million people globally are poisoned annually by pesticides—10,000 of whom die.

†It is not just wheat that has been refused. The European Economic Community in 1989 refused U.S. beef because of high levels of antibiotics. The chemicals strengthen drug-resistant bacteria that cause human illness. Russia and Japan refused drought-weakened corn with Aflatoxion—a cancer-causing fungus. The Food and Drug Administration allows infected corn to be mixed with healthy corn for use as feed. Whether Aflatoxion will show up in milk remains to be seen.

best of the world's hundreds of varieties of corn to produce a super hybrid. The hybrids are so superior that today in America and other developed nations only one or two varieties are grown (the same is true of wheat). The concern is that when corn blight was found in Florida, it destroyed one-third of all the acreage in that state. Since every plant was exactly the same, the disease spread rapidly from field to field.[*] What causes or ends a blight is not yet fully understood. But unlike times past when only some fields of a specific type of crop were lost to disease, the world, and the United States in particular, is very susceptible to a catastrophic crop failure that may take several years to overcome. In fact, it may be overcome only when large enough volumes of "new" seeds that are not sensitive to the blight in question are made available.

Of course, the world's staple foods are most affected. Of the tens of thousands of plant forms on Earth, 140 are edible, with only 40 types of food that are common. Only seven types are staple foods (e.g., corn, wheat, rice, and oats), and make up 90 percent of all food consumed. Because of their importance, all have been developed into hybrids. Since there is no reserve of hybrid replacements, what happens if a blight does break out? What happens to 70 percent of the world's food energy (grains) if a new disease develops, water is less abundant through misuse or widespread drought (see Figure IV-6), or a small climatic change occurs? Clearly, no place on Earth is guaranteed a bountiful harvest. Famine can strike anywhere at anytime if the Earth's delicate balance is disturbed.

It would not take much cooling to have profound effects on worldwide food production. Certainly, "freezing" temperatures are not required. *Science News* reported in September 1985 that corn dies when exposed to temperatures of 54°F for six days. An average seasonal temperature drop of only 3.5°F would halve the wheat production in the United States and Canada. A change of 9°F would do the same to corn and rice production.

---

[*]History provided a lesson that apparently was not learned. Two varieties of potato so out-performed other strains that they became the only varieties planted in Ireland. The potato blight of 1841 caused 1 million people to migrate to America while millions more died of starvation.

Figure IV-6. The Drought of 1988

The effect of the 1987–1988 drought is shown as residents of San Jose, California, observed their bone-dry reservoir and river bed. The far-reaching drought caused Minnesota, North and South Dakota, and Montana to lose half their harvests. Nevada had its driest year on record, and the Army Corps of Engineers had to dredge the Mississippi River to free 1,000 stranded barges. Continued drought blows away so much valuable topsoil that vast areas could be permanently lost to farming.

One development of man's advancing technology that may cause widespread climatic change is the destruction of the tropical rain forests. These tall, dense forests contain 1 billion people but only 6 percent of the Earth's land mass. The areas are lush forests because the thick growth catches rainfall and then slowly releases it back to the environment, thus encouraging additional rainfall elsewhere. The poor soil of the tropics cannot reproduce the forest because 95 percent of the nutrients of these areas are contained in the dead and living plants of the forest itself. After being cleared erosion quickly washes away what little topsoil there is.

Because a tropical forest cannot replenish itself when the forest is cleared, the environment, locally and worldwide, is changed forever. The importance of the tropical forest cannot be overstated as 80 percent of the world's vegetation is contained in these jungles. These plants remove carbon dioxide (CO_2) from the atmosphere and produce life-sustaining oxygen. Clearing of the forests means not only that CO_2 is no longer removed, but also that a large quantity of CO_2 is produced by the burning of the wood. CO_2 in the atmosphere causes the Earth to retain more of its heat (the greenhouse effect) and thus to become warmer (changing the climate).[*]

After a tropical forest is cleared, the soil erodes so much that within a few years nothing will grow and the area reverts to desert. This is what happened in the past to North Africa and is happening today in areas surrounding Ethiopia. Since firewood and grazing land are needed by the poor and malnourished, forests are cleared. Unfortunately, clearing expands deserts and causes more severe droughts, which in turn require the clearing of more forests. As the CO_2 levels increase and as less moisture is put back into the atmosphere, the world's climate changes, affecting the temperate lands of the northern latitudes as well.[†]

It is not just Africa that is destroying its tropical rain forest; Nigeria lost 90 percent, Ghana 80 percent, and Brazil 98 percent of its coastal forests. Malaysia, Thailand, Haiti, and the Philippines

---

[*]Presently only 1/30th of 1 percent of our atmosphere is CO_2, and 1 percent is water vapor (not to be confused with relative humidity, which is the ratio of moisture present to the maximum that could be present). These two gases "trap" the Earth's heat from being radiated out to space. Were it not for these two gases, the Earth's average temperature would drop from 60°F to -18°F (a hot summer's day would not get above the freezing point of 32°F). Of the two gases, CO_2 definitely is more effective at preventing radiation losses. Thus, even small changes in the concentration of CO_2 can have profound effects on the Earth.

[†]Increases in atmospheric CO_2 are now thought to be contributing to global warming, which has caused six of the warmest years on record to occur in the 1980s. This warming trend is raising sea temperatures. Hurricanes derive their energy from water over 70°F. Thus, the biggest hurricane on record, Gilbert in 1988 (packing 200 mph winds that left 2.3 million homeless), was partially blamed on the destruction of rain forests.

have all but depleted their forests. In all, 144,000 acres of tropical forest are being flattened each day, with 16,000 acres a day being destroyed in Central America. In the past 30 years, 40 percent of the forests were destroyed. Thirty years from now there may be no forests left. Already the loss of Panamanian forests has decreased annual rainfall by 17 inches (equal to the total rainfall of San Francisco, California).

Other forest losses are blamed for the growth of the Sahara Desert and melting of the pack ice at the poles (due to changes in CO_2 levels). The effects are real, and the consequences are serious and not easily reversed. The 200 billion tons of CO_2 that man has added thus far to the atmosphere would require 900 years for removal by the Earth's ecosystem. No end of CO_2 production is foreseeable, and the consequences are becoming increasingly unsettling.

Observe the following quotation from *U.S. News & World Report* (March 31, 1986):[30] "...Siberia could be the breadbasket of the world, New York may be at the bottom of the sea and one fourth [sic] of all species of wildlife may be extinct."

Thus, plagues can be brought about by natural causes, or they can be caused by our own mismanagement and greed or by terrorism. Conditions seem poised to cascade upon us very quickly.

If floods, earthquakes, and famines came to pass, is there any reason to doubt that disease, pestilence, and plague could run rampant throughout our society? The above discussion of *natural* disasters does not even consider man-made plagues, such as devastating chemical warfare or experimental life forms that modern science is trying to create.

PLAGUES

A few years ago genetic engineering companies were able to raise 50 times their value in stock issues, but many are now in trouble.* They have not made a profit because most have not

---

*In the last 20 years, more than 600 biotech companies have been started in the United States. All but a few have shown continuous losses.

made a useful risk free product. How can they guarantee that new experimental life forms can never escape from the laboratory and invade society? Is it possible that companies desperate to cut costs and to show a profit may become sloppy in the nongovernment-regulated procedures that prevent new "life" from leaking out? Genetic scientists have made life in the past, or altered life, to eat oil and make chemicals. The problem is safety: Too often, man has introduced nonindigenous life forms in the hope of improving some minor problem only to have it create a major problem instead. The list of such mistakes is endless, from the Japanese beetle and the gypsy moth which cause major defoliation in the East, to walking catfish and jungle weeds which crowd out useful fish and plants in the South, to vegetable-eating snails and killer bees which displace the efficient food pollinating honey bee in the Southwest.

It is clear that "man" is not knowledgeable enough or careful enough to be entrusted with determining what new life forms should be introduced. For instance, the USDA, after receiving strong lobbying pressure, has approved the field testing (in the open environment) of a genetically altered virus that prevents frost damage to plants by changing the properties of the water within the plant. This is likely to save strawberry growers millions of dollars a year. Of course, no requirement has been imposed to notify the consumer that these strawberries contain what is believed to be a "harmless" virus. Remember, DDT, carbon tetrachloride, and stain-eating enzymes were also once thought to be harmless. Now that this life form has been created and released, a new concern has alarmed scientists. If this virus is blown into the atmosphere (as it is bound to be), it may inhibit the formation of ice crystals in the upper atmosphere. The ice crystals are necessary for cloud formation. Without clouds there is no chance of rain, and the environment will be permanently altered.

This case comes to light because it has government approval, but many tests are conducted with no regulation whatsoever. For example, Techamerica Inc. of Omaha developed a genetically engineered organism that was field tested on 1,350 pigs in 1984, six months before the application was filed for a government license. Surely, government regulation is a far cry from protection, but what hope is there of control when the regulatory agencies are not even involved?

As this was being written, the first man-made (genetically engineered) bacteria was released into the environment without Environmental Protection Agency (EPA) approval. An Advanced Genetic Sciences, Inc. spokesman stated that they did not consider "the use of the bacteria in an open air roof to be an 'environmental release.'" However, no precautions were implemented to prevent insects or wind from transporting the bacteria from the test plants to the open environment.

Was this an act of stupidity or the result of economic pressure caused by repeated delays in obtaining an EPA outdoor testing permit? If some profit-seeking company makes the wrong bug and that bacteria or virus escapes and starts attacking people, or vital food, would science have any means to control it? It would seem unlikely because new bugs are purposely made to be very different from the old ones. Certainly, any means of control that may be needed could not be developed fast enough to prevent catastrophic losses.

As evidence of how difficult new diseases can be to understand and control, consider that as recently as 1979 it was generally accepted that advances in medical knowledge eliminated the threat of widespread infectious disease in the developed world.[31] Then, in 1981, the first case of AIDS was diagnosed.

Science does not always grasp the depth of its lack of knowledge, as expressed by Surgeon General Koop on January 7, 1987: "At first a cure or vaccine for AIDS was thought to be on the horizon, and then [we thought it would take] five years, and then [we thought we would have one] by the year 2000. It is now clear that the AIDS virus is so complex that a vaccine will never be found." Like the common cold virus, the AIDS virus changes quickly; different strains have evolved, and each could require a different vaccine. Again, like the common cold, AIDS has treatments but no cure. Unlike the common cold however the AIDS-infected person will surely die.

The statistics for AIDS are alarming. The number of reported AIDS cases has been doubling every 13 months. The World Health Organization (WHO) has reported a total of 133,000 cases, 82,764 of which are in the United States, with 10 million carriers of the virus. WHO suspects that at least half of AIDS cases remain unreported, but other organizations have claimed that the actual number of cases is 10 times higher. However even the more conservative numbers are overwhelming. New York City had 4,848 cases in 1988 with 415,000 carriers; it expects 109,000 cases by 1991. The United States expects 270,000 cases in 1991 and 450,000 in 1993. Again, these are conservative estimates. The cost of this disease to taxpayers, not counting lost productivity, is a staggering $40 billion.

The worst news is that the American Medical Association's (AMA) insistence that AIDS cannot be acquired through casual contact may be misleading. New evidence shows that AIDS, like the common cold,* may be spread by any body fluid including perspiration transferred in a handshake. The Centers for Disease Control (CDC) in Atlanta has acknowledged that AIDS has been spread by saliva during biting and through oral sex. The CDC also acknowledged that six nurses contracted AIDS after being splashed with blood, even though they had no cuts or breaks in the skin. Small wonder that of 4,000 dentists surveyed in Chicago, only four would accept as a patient someone with AIDS. It is now known that up to 70 percent of AIDS patients participating in sexual activity transmitted AIDS to their spouses regardless of their sexual preferences. Although attacked by special interest groups and members of the AMA, Masters and Johnson reported in 1988 that AIDS can be spread by casual contact, including media such as toilets and food.

Although earlier cases disproportionately affected homosexuals and drug users, AIDS is now a serious threat to the heterosexual community.[32] An African strain (HIV-2) seems to be as easily transmitted by heterosexual relations as by homosexual

---

*Unlike the common cold, AIDS-infected body fluid must contact a break or thinning of the recipient's skin to pose a threat.

relations. In Zambia, more than half of the army is infected, as are a third of the young men in its capitol. Of the adult populations of Uganda, the Congo, Rwanda, and Tanzania, 12 to 20 percent are infected. The African strain has recently spread to Haiti. If this strain spreads to the United States, the number of AIDS victims will increase substantially.

The problem with AIDS is there is still so much that is unknown. Even the time between exposure and testing positive (believed to be one year) is not known. Estimations for the incubation period of the disease have continually been moved upward. The longer the incubation period, the greater the chance of transmitting the disease. WHO reported in January 1989 that the average incubation period was 12.5 years—longer than most relationships and many marriages. The prescribed use of condoms for protection may be misleading because membrane condoms are porous to the microscopic virus. Although latex condoms are not porous, they can break. Condoms have long been considered only 90 percent effective as a form of birth control.* A University of Miami study shows that 16 percent of the couples that always used latex condoms have transmitted the AIDS virus to their mates.†

The most effective means of transmission is blood transfer, which occurs in sharing hypodermic syringes. Dr. Theresa Crenshaw, a member of President Reagan's 1988 Commission on AIDS, stated her belief that AIDS could be spread by mosquitoes.[33] In a separate report, Dr. Robert Gallo, one of the discoverers of the AIDS virus at the National Institute of Health (NIH), demonstrated that the AIDS virus can live for extended periods of time in mosquitoes that feed on AIDS-tainted blood. The only good news about AIDS is that so far, mosquito transmission has not been substantiated. However that may change. In 1985 the supermosquito *Aedes Albopictus,* or tiger mosquito was accidently imported from Madagascar to Texas. This aggressive insect bites night and day, attacking each host several times. Unlike native

---

*Ten percent of the women whose partners always use condoms have an unwanted pregnancy.

†This study was conducted for a relatively short period. The probability of transmission is likely to increase with time.

mosquitoes, the tiger has the unusual ability to transmit disease through its saliva and eggs, making its offspring infectious from birth. In part because this hardy mosquito is highly resistant to all commonly used insecticides, it has already spread east to the Atlantic and north to Chicago. Even if the disease is never transmitted by insects, AIDS has the potential to be the worst threat to public health since the bubonic plague (black death) of 1350.*

One might suspect that man brings plagues onto himself through overcrowding, unsanitary living conditions, pollution, promiscuity, uncontrolled introduction of pests, and other means. Could man create a Great Plague through genetic engineering, scientific accident, or stupidity? Yes. Could a Great Plague result from warfare or the use of biological weapons? Yes. Could a great natural plague be caused by people being homeless and hungry? Yes. Does not plague usually break out in weakened or destroyed societies? We never eliminated the bubonic plague, which exists in California and in other places. Every year, animals in rural mountain areas contract this dreaded disease. These animals are watched closely, so few people are infected. But that does not prevent the possibility of a major infestation and devastating outbreak of epidemic proportions. Of course, we would all like to think that since nothing like this has happened recently (in our lifetime), it is not likely to happen again. If Nostradamus and John have anything in common, it is that they claim that these disasters will occur.

ANTARCTICA

The instabilities mentioned above may not be completely unrelated. If you measured the Earth from space, you would find that it is pear shaped. This shape is caused in part by the rotation of the Earth, which through centrifugal forces caused the equator to bulge. But this shape is also evidence of rather significant and

---

*Health Secretary Otis Bowen in February 1987 stated: "We face...a worldwide death toll in the tens of millions. ...the Bubonic Plague [would] pale by comparison."

major past Earth movements. Think of the force that was required to separate Europe from America or to split apart the single super-continent of Pangaea or move Antarctica from the equator to the South Pole.

What violent forces caused Ice Ages? For a long time, it was believed that Ice Ages took tens of thousands of years to start and equally long to recede. Although the recession is relatively slow, scientists have recently found that Ice Ages can occur quickly—in weeks—and then self-perpetuate their growth for many years.

Antarctica has about the same land mass as all of North America: the United States, Canada, and Mexico. So, Antarctica is not a small place. In contrast, the North Pole has no land mass, just frozen ocean. The Arctic Ocean froze because of the land around it, which stopped it from receiving the thermal currents necessary to keep it more temperate. The big block of ice in Antarctica used to be much larger before the Ice Age recession started about 10,000 years ago. That ice was so immense that the roundness of the Earth was altered by its great weight. The amount of compression is 600 meters, or approximately 2,000 feet, or roughly just over one-third of a mile.

The ice on Antarctica keeps melting because we are in the retreating edge of an Ice Age. Once in recession, it accelerates its rate of retreat as more ocean melts and starts absorbing rather than reflecting sunlight, causing further warming and melting. For example, Columbia, the last of Alaska's 52 tidewater gla-ciers, is receding from the sea at the rate of almost three-quarters of a mile a year. This is four times faster than just six years ago, and the rate is still increasing. Because the 40-mile-long glacier is becoming shorter, there is less resistance, and so it is moving faster. This means that even if exposing additional heat-absorb-ing water does not cause more ice to melt, the ice is becoming thinner from faster movement and is becoming lighter from its thinning and its shortening (see Figure IV-7).

For the last 15 years, the bay ice in Antarctica has been stead-ily receding. Although Antarctica receives more sunlight during its summer than the equator does, 97 percent of the energy received from the sun is reflected back into outer space by the white coloring of the ice pack. Now that 6 percent of the bay ice has melted, not only may it not refreeze, but it will absorb more heat, which will contribute to more heating and melting. The rocky crust of the Earth has been deformed by the original massive ice sheet and has been solidified in place. But the hand holding down the cork on the liquid mantle of the Earth is being removed as this ice melts.

Figure IV-7. Columbia Glacier

A 300-foot-long iceberg breaking off from the Columbia Glacier. This action can be witnessed hundreds of times per day as the last of Alaska's tidewater glaciers recedes from the sea, a clear sign that the climate is becoming warmer.

Three dire possibilities could occur to melt the ice caps. Each of these possibilities would have devastating effects on planet Earth.

Possibility 1

The first possibility concerns one of the most spectacular events in the universe: the supernova. Is it possible that a supernova could go off in the southern hemispheric sky? If it did, would it disperse enough heat and light to melt Antarctica? That is very possible. Since there is little observation of the southern sky, astronomers do not have a good grasp of how many candidates for a supernova exist or how far from the Earth they may be. Science has postulated the creation of an instantaneous supernova in different parts of the sky: stars called red giants, such as Betelgeuse, that are too large for their mass and are collapsing.* In astronomical time, this collapse happens instantaneously. It could become a supernova in a couple of thousand years, or it could explode tomorrow; science does not know all the answers. Could a supernova melt the caps at both Poles? Absolutely! If the Earth warmed just 3°F, the caps would melt. An increase of 20 degrees would melt them relatively quickly. Shining light directly on the caps day and night, summer and winter, would cause them to melt at an unprecedented rate.

In Chapter II, Nostradamus' predictions were discussed. Recently, another two centuries of his prophesies were uncovered. These are called the black centuries because of their content. He published the other centuries himself, but he did not want to publish these; instead, he hid them in the walls of his house. However, he must have wanted them to be published eventually or he would have destroyed them. In these works, Nostradamus talked about events worse than floods, pestilence, and disease. He talked about "when night becomes day."[34] Could a supernova qualify for his explanation of how night becomes day because there would be two suns in the sky? If there were two suns, not only would the weather patterns be unrecognizable, but the entire Earth would become dangerously hot.

---

*Betelgeuse is so large that the sun and the orbits of all the planets out to Mars fit within its diameter.

Nostradamus said and the Bible states that after God comes back to Earth, the planet will be remade and it will have peace and tranquility for 1,000 years. At the end of 1,000 years, the Earth will be destroyed. Calculations of the places scientists think are going to become supernovas indicate that they are not likely to cause the aforementioned event because they are a couple of hundred light years away, which is too distant. However, if a supernova occurred, the first impact we would experience is the light and heat. The second effect would be the impact of the material released by the blast.

How fast would the mass move out of the supernova? Although it would move at tremendous speeds, its rate would be slower than that of light, which travels at 186,000 miles per second. The mass of a supernova has been measured to expand at approximately 4,000 to 6,000 miles per second. The time difference between the impact of the light and the blast material would be 1,000 years if the supernova occurred approximately 30 to 45 light years away (250 trillion miles). Supernovas happen in the universe regularly; in our galaxy they occur about once every 100 years. The last supernova to occur in our Milky Way Galaxy was on the far side of the galaxy and was recorded almost 400 years ago in 1604. When will one of the billions of stars on our side of the Milky Way become a supernova?

Possibility 2

A second dire possibility is that a volcano could erupt in the volcanically active continent of Antarctica, throwing out tons of black dust. The recent Mexican eruption of *El Chichón* produced more ash than Mt. St. Helens, and the ash circled the globe several times before settling to Earth. The air currents around Antarctica rotate clockwise around the Pole. If the dust followed a circular pattern, it could cover large areas of polar ice. Then, by changing from white to black, the ice would absorb 97 percent of the light, instead of reflecting 97 percent of it. Why worry about carbon dioxide and the "greenhouse effect" in 50 years? Worldwide disaster will not take that long. When the time is right, the caps can melt very quickly. What happens if the ice melts at the Pole?

If either Pole melted, the other one would also melt because the whole Earth would become warmer as more reflected light became absorbed.

If the Poles melted, how much water would be added to the oceans? There would be enough to raise the oceans 197 feet. This is significant because coastal areas represent 12 percent of the Earth's land area and two-thirds of the world's people. The population of the world is centered in cities located on trade routes. Normally, the trade route cities are built six feet above high tide, as in New York, Boston, Philadelphia, Los Angeles, San Diego, and San Francisco. Therefore, if only a few percent of the ice melted, cataclysmic repercussions would result. Florida, Louisiana, and many other places would suddenly be under water. All of San Francisco would not be under water; the hills would still show. But a city is people, transportation, communication, gas, electricity, and sewer services.

Without these necessities, a modern city would cease to exist even if parts of the city could survive the immediate effect of the rising water. The cities of the world, especially the biggest, the oldest, the best of them, can be destroyed by a partial melting of the caps. That would cause economic, redistribution, and food problems, the likes of which the world has never known. Even WWII could not compare. But those problems would be minor compared with the effects on the weather and the Earth's crust.

The weather pattern of the world is dominated by the effects of the Earth being a heat engine. This heat engine takes cold, heavy air from the Poles and pushes it to the equator as the equator's hot, light air is driven over the cold air on its journey to the Poles. The rotation of the Earth then perpetuates what we call the jet stream. Central and Southern California had virtually no rain for two years during the drought of 1975–1976 because the jet stream was a little bit too far north, producing arid Southern California weather in San Francisco. It rained buckets up in Oregon during the same period because Oregon was still north of the jet stream and therefore had normal weather. Similar problems were experienced in the Southeast during the drought of 1986. The jet stream being too far north caused the worst drought in the area's history. The result was water rationing, destruction of 75 percent of North Carolina's corn crop, 90 percent of Alabama's wheat crop, and the death of 750,000 Georgia chickens.

So, the 180-mph jet stream (one each in the northern and southern hemispheres) controls our weather. Warm air going up and over mountains and cooling or meeting cold air causes precipitation. Without a jet stream, there would be no wind, without wind there would be no weather fronts, and without weather fronts there would be no rain. Without the Poles covered with reflective ice, the temperature gradient across the Earth that we have taken for granted would not exist. Therefore, the heat engine would not exist, eliminating the jet stream, the wind, weather fronts, and rain. We would not have a weather pattern, or at least not the weather pattern that we know.

What would this mean? The great Pacific coast states with their tall, lush forests would no longer have precipitation. The wheat belt might revert to the Dust Bowl Era of the 1930s when nothing would grow. It is not possible to forecast accurately the specifics of such a catastrophic change. Citrus fruits might have to be grown in Alaska, and snow peas might become extinct, as could water crops such as rice, cotton, and corn. How long would it take to relocate the people, the machinery, and the equipment to make parts of Alaska arable to grow wheat? Who would invest in such a changing climate in the first few years?

With such vast and uncertain changes taking place, individuals would not risk the investment but would turn to their governments for aid and guidance. Governments would try to encourage action if they knew what action to take and if they were not in dire straits, but with so much economic loss and chaos governments would not be able to establish useful long-term programs for some time. If governments could not feed their people and their cities were no longer usable, would society maintain its status quo?

Consider why Argentina attacked England. Was it because the Falklands were suddenly a necessity, or because the Argentine government wanted to turn the public eye away from runaway inflation, economic downturns, 40 percent unemployment, and food shortages? Countries do not often go to war when the people are content. They go to war when there is poverty, no solution to their problems, and a need to create a cause to unite their people. As a side effect of war, some of the population is killed, making it more likely to feed those who survive.

If the Poles melted, the world would have severe problems indeed. However, destruction of the major cities and drastic changes in the Earth's weather are only part of the argument. A more significant effect would also be caused by melting even part of the ice caps. However, it is necessary to review some background information before examining the balance of the polar consequences.

The Richter Scale, which is used to measure the intensity of earthquakes, is exponential. Therefore, an increase of one in the rating indicates a 10 fold increase in the force of an earthquake. When Richter retired a few years ago, he was asked by the media if earthquake-proof buildings could truly withstand a magnitude-8 earthquake. He answered "Absolutely not. No building in this world could withstand a number 8 earthquake."

He said that what is meant by "earthquake-proof" is survival of a structure 20 to 40 miles away from the epicenter when the earthquake hits (see Figure IV-8). The closer a structure is to the epicenter, the more likely it will be severely damaged. At the epicenter, no structure could survive a major earthquake. Not a single tree may be left standing at the epicenter of a magnitude-8 earthquake. In fact, a solid rock might not survive such an earthquake because for 400 feet on both sides of the fault over the epicenter, the ground may plow. In plowing, it would break and shift. The violent action could drive even large boulders many feet underground.

Science is still learning about the effects of large earthquakes. Liquefaction is a big problem that was only first studied after the 1964 Alaskan quake destroyed many earthquake-proof buildings. In that quake, the ground actually turned to quicksand through a shaking motion where high soil moisture levels were present. That is one reason why bedrock is a relatively safe place in an earthquake, if it is not at the epicenter.

Figure IV-8. Freeway After the 1971 Earthquake

Modern buildings and freeways are designed to be "earthquake-proof." The relatively mild 6.5-magnitude San Fernando earthquake in 1971 was 500 times weaker then the 8.3-magnitude 1906 quake. Examining the damage to the modern Golden State Freeway, one must wonder just how much science really understands about the forces of earthquakes.

The 1906 earthquake in San Francisco was actually centered about 30 miles north at Point Reyes (see Figure IV-9). In fact, the shock was stronger in Santa Rosa than it was in San Francisco, but San Francisco had fires, which made its damage worse. San Francisco sits next to the San Andreas Fault, which creates large earthquakes and slips as one tectonic plate slides past another. The big 8.0 earthquake anticipated on the San Andreas Fault would cause an 18-foot slip, as did the 1906 earthquake (see Figure IV-10). Other quakes along the San Andreas Fault have caused even larger movements, such as the 1857 quake north of Los Angeles that resulted in a 30-foot lunge. Although scientists think that they understand the *basics* of the West Coast seismic activity, they still confess bewilderment concerning less frequent but more devastating East Coast earthquakes. The power of these quakes is exemplified by the 1812 shaker in Missouri that was 20 times stronger than the 1906 San Francisco quake. This quake *lost* the town of New Madrid. As the land rose and then sank 15 feet, the flow of the Mississippi River reversed and then permanently changed course, and the landscape was altered for hundreds of miles. The quake was felt so far away that it caused church bells to ring in Boston. A repeat performance, which is expected in the 1990s, will affect seven states and 12-million people.

Figure IV-9. San Francisco After the 1906 Earthquake

This scene resembles the destruction of an A-bomb during WWII. The damage was caused by a magnitude-8.3 quake that destroyed one-and two-story buildings. The damage that will be caused to "earthquake-resistant" skyscrapers by the next major quake is uncertain.

Figure IV-10. Split Fence on the San Andreas Fault

This fence was originally built on a continuous straight line. During the 1906 quake, the Pacific plate (foreground) jumped 18 feet to the left. The quake (equal in energy release to a 15-megaton H-bomb) released more energy in 30 seconds than San Francisco power plants have generated in the 83 years since then.

Figure IV-11. A Building that Meets Other Specifications

The strange structure that surrounds this building is a double set of steel girders
to protect the occupants from earthquakes. The building was built to earthquake
standards, but the scientists that work in the building petitioned to have the extra
protection added. The building is owned by the U.S. Geological Survey Group,
which studies the effects of major earthquakes.

Herein lies the problem. The facts indicate the possibility for unexpected and undefinable events. The real consideration about melting the caps is that their complete removal would not be necessary to create profound repercussions. It may not be necessary to remove most, or even much, of the ice pack. The weight of ice that was originally on the South Pole was enormous compared with what it is today. As mentioned earlier, this great weight originally caused the depression of 600 meters, or one-third of a mile, in the Earth's crust. If this weight were removed or decreased, the continental crust would no longer be in balance with the Earth's liquid core. Thus, the Earth would have to readjust itself. As a result, it would move not 18 feet, but 1,800 feet (1/3 of a mile), 100 times more movement than resulted from the 1906 San Francisco earthquake. But the movement would not be a slip action along several miles of the fault line; it would be a whole continent picking up and moving out.

Antarctica is the size of North America: 6 million square miles. However, the Antarctic plate extends over 21 million square miles. Multiply that by a 0.33-mile movement, and you come up with 7 million cubic miles of adjustment. When Mt. St. Helens blew its top, it threw out 0.7 cubic mile of ashes. The result was that most of the mountain was missing (see Figure IV-12). All the dust that spread around the Earth, covered the other states, and caused people to shovel ashes for hundreds of miles around was 0.7 cubic mile. Compare that with a movement of 7 million cubic miles, which is 10 million times greater. What would happen when the whole continent moved out one-third of a mile? It would create a void or a space 7 million cubic miles in size. The northern continents would have to make up that difference by coming together; in doing so, they would be forced to overlap.

The result would not be a normal earthquake. First of all, it would be worldwide. If the Antarctic continent moved, the northern continents along the plate lines would buckle to take up the slack. Mountains would be created where there were none, and *tsunamis* would circle the globe. The waves that were six feet over high tide that caused houses to be washed into the sea and also caused so much damage to the shoreline are microscopic compared with the seismic waves that would be caused by tectonic plate movement on this scale.

Figure IV-12. Destruction Near Mt. St. Helens

Visitors still come to view the damage years after the Mt. St. Helens explosion. The above debris was once a lush timber forest located several miles from the site of the explosion.

The Pacific Ocean off the California coast is 15,000 feet deep, and it covers 6,000 miles to Japan, 3,000 miles to Alaska, and 9,000 miles to Antarctica. If 1 millionth of 1 percent of that water rose and came toward California, a *tsunami* hundreds of feet high would wash over many smaller mountains. Do you think that this would not be truly devastating or that such a possibility is far-fetched?

Consider these recent reports:

1. The Krakatoa earthquake of 1883 created a massive tsunami that circumnavigated the globe and took 36,000 lives. The volcanic explosion was heard 2,200 miles away.[1]

2. In Pakistan a 100-foot tidal wave caused by a storm killed tens of thousands of people in June 1985, just 15 years after the same area was hit by a similar wave.

3. New studies on the mountains of Hawaii show that the islands were hit by 1,000-foot waves at least twice in recent history, which deposited coral from the ocean bottom to mountainsides 2,000 feet above sea level.[35]

If the Antarctic plate moved out, the whole world would adjust and move and buckle. The effect would be millions of times greater than an "8" on the Richter Scale. Is an earthquake of this magnitude incomprehensible? Of course! Would it create incredible devastation? Absolutely!

Nostradamus said that an earthquake will be felt worldwide, and it will destroy every building that exists. The Bible says that when the great quake comes, not an island will be left in the sea, many nations of the Earth will cease to exist, and no mountain will be left in its place. Those are pretty strong words. They seemed so incomprehensible that until now they were just meaningless words. But scientifically, we can explain how this could happen.

Possibility 3

The third dire possibility for melting the ice caps and causing the destruction of cities, lack of rain, famine, and plagues has its roots with Fatima, (discussed in detail in Chapter V), Nostradamus, and comets.

More comets have come close to the Earth in the last 6 years than in the last 200 years, according to science. The closest rendezvous of a comet happened in the summer of 1984, but it was not detected until three days after it had passed. The greatest of all predictable comets is Halley's, which passes near the Earth every 76 years. It appeared again in 1986, which is the year the nine planets aligned with each other in their orbits.

This unusual alignment of all the planets occurs rarely because some planets take hundreds of years to orbit around the sun. Nostradamus said that "when the comet makes its run"[36] will be the start of the great drought and that the drought would cause a world wide famine. John does not name a year, but stated that for a period of 1260 days or 3-1/2 years (Rev. 11:1–3), two prophets will be granted the power to prevent rain during the days of their prophesying. This is to be an unprecedented drought as even the River Euphrates will run dry (Rev. 16:12), an event that has never before been known to occur. Coincidentally, all the planets came into perfect alignment (i.e., a straight line) in 1986 for the first time in 280,000 years. The last occurrence of such an event was way before recorded history. The rarity of this phenomenon dramatizes the Bible's prediction that the Second Coming of Christ would be announced by a sign in the stars and the planets. What could be more eventful than the positioning of all nine planets in a straight line at the same time that the largest known comet was to pass by the Earth. Has this all been predetermined?

In the past, the sight of Halley's comet has been so awesome that startled viewers have feared for their lives. But the visibility of the 4.5-mile-long comet depends on how close it comes to the Earth. On this trip, when Halley's comet was closest to the Earth, it was on the opposite side of the sun from the Earth, thus making it less visible than in the past. As a result, Halley's produced the dullest showing of its 30 recorded visits since 240 B.C.

Other visitors from space have been more spectacular. About 30,000 years ago, a small meteorite struck the Earth near present-day Flagstaff, Arizona. The impact created a 4,000-foot crater, released the energy of a 15-megaton H-bomb, and killed most living things within a 25-mile diameter. It may also have knocked the Earth slightly off its axis, producing its wobble. That meteor was only 135 feet in diameter. At present, at least 40 known asteroids over 3,300 feet in diameter regularly cross the Earth's orbit, the largest are several million times larger than the Flagstaff meteorite. Just think what a 3,300 foot diameter meteor, 15 thousand times larger than the Flagstaff meteorite, could do if even a fragment were to strike the Earth.[*]

---

[*]This possibility became all too real in 1989. On March 31 astronomers spotted an unknown asteroid eight days after it past within only a few hundred thousand miles of the Earth. The half-mile-wide hunk of rock, traveling at 46,000 miles per hour, could have created a 10-mile-wide impact crater or produced a tidal wave 300 feet high. There were two other close encounters in 1989 that were discovered only after the objects passed. How many close encounters were not observed is not known.

Remember also that one of the real fears of an atomic war is the effect of "nuclear winter" caused by the huge amounts of dust that would be thrown into the atmosphere for long periods. Actually, the "nuclear winter" consideration grew out of new evidence that the dinosaurs were killed worldwide by just such an instantaneous and dramatic climate change caused by a meteor impact. A large impact, it is believed, could have created enough atmospheric dust to block out a large portion of the sun's light. If this dust stayed airborne, it could have brought on the start of an Ice Age in a matter of weeks and killed many forms of plant life. It is believed that just such a meteor ended the dinosaurs' 100-million-year dominance of the Earth.[*]

By studying fossils, scientists have found that every 26 million years 70 percent of all life forms are eliminated on our planet. This phenomenon is thought to be caused by "Nemesis," an elliptically orbiting "dark star" companion to the sun. It is believed that every 26 million years Nemesis makes a periodic close pass to the sun (still 1,000 times further away than Pluto), and its gravity knocks "space junk" out of the delicately balanced Oort Belt. The Oort Belt is located at the very edge of our planetary (solar) system and is the source of all comets.[†]

Periodic comet/meteor showers have produced the craters of the moon and of other planets. A 5-mile diameter comet colliding with the Earth would be equal to a 100-million-megaton explosion and would create a crater 100 miles in diameter. Although craters

---

[*]A localized example of nuclear winter was observed in Klamath, California, in the summer of 1987. Severe drought caused massive forest fires, which sent vast amounts of smoke into the atmosphere. So much sunlight was blocked that car headlights had to be used at noon, and the temperature dropped 50°F below normal.

[†]The Oort Belt surrounds the solar system with 100 billion large chunks of leftover "space junk" that are 1 to 10 miles in diameter. The debris stays in place because of a delicate balance among three forces. The sun's distant pull of gravity is exactly equal to the pushing force of the sun's solar wind plus the background gravity of the galaxies. These forces are extremely weak. Thus, any additional gravitational force, such as the passing of Nemesis, can cause them to fall out of the Oort Belt toward the sun and the planets. Nemesis is believed to be 88,000 times farther from the sun than the Earth.

on Earth are destroyed by erosion, 28 major-impact craters ranging from 1 to 100 miles in diameter still exist. Pictures sent back from the exploration satellite Voyager, have shown that the rings of Saturn, Jupiter, and Uranus were probably caused by the tremendous impact of a comet smashing into an orbiting moon. The only thing that remains is the dust (varying in size from grains of sand to boulders) of the impact. The oceans and weather destroy the impact of craters on Earth, but the Earth's stronger gravity has caused it to be struck by more major space junk than has struck the moon.

What if the alignment of the planets caused a gravitational pull strong enough to cause distant comets to go off course or to fall out of the Oort cloud? Even a small course change after several years could cause distant objects to approach the sun. The relative closeness of the Earth to the sun presents the possibility that such objects may come very close to our planet.

Places of religious apparitions such as Bayside, New York,[*] make it clear that a comet is the Biblically prophesied warning. According to Bayside, this comet will pass directly between the Earth and the sun so that the Earth will be shadowed from the sun's light by its tail.

In 1985 the United States moved a solar satellite off course to meet with a comet that arrived before Halley's. The Japanese, Europeans, and Russians sent space probes specifically to observe Halley's comet to try to understand what makes up the comet that loses 1-million tons of material a day to form its tail. A lot of evidence indicates that if the Earth passed through the tail of a comet, which can be millions of miles long, much dust would be collected, affecting the ionosphere. The ionosphere affects our rain pattern and the northern lights. The result could be atmospheric disturbances and extreme weather on Earth, with

---

[*]Bayside, New York, is the location of many apparitions, which have been reported since 1973. Although witnessed by very few, these apparitions deliver messages similar to that of Fatima. Indeed, these messages tend to explain the significance and consequences of "the miracle of the sun," which is discussed in detail in Chapter V.

heavy rain worldwide or severe drought for several years. If something like this happens, we will have catastrophes in many areas, especially regarding food production. Even the Great Plains of America could resemble Ethiopia.

The Bayside story is about a warning that is both frightening and unanticipated. Perhaps the fact that it is unanticipated will demonstrate to the world that science can more easily explain events after they occur than predict them. Science can put men on the moon or blow up the world. Science can feed distant people, transmit video images around the world, and create computer brains the size of a postage stamp. Mankind is very impressed with its scientific accomplishments.

In the Portuguese village of Fatima,[*] apparitions were recorded in 1917. In addition, verbal messages were given simultaneously to three small children. The surviving Fatima seer has recently revealed that the flaming ball seen by 71,000 people at Fatima was not the sun, but a fireball comet that is going to have a close encounter with the Earth. This comet will appear seven times brighter and hotter than the sun, and it will dry up the oceans and the lakes and the rivers. It will burn one-third of the trees and grasses, and will kill one-third of the fish in the sea.

This agrees with Biblical prophecy, which says exactly the same thing. In fact, the Bible goes one step further and says that we will know when the endtime has come because there will be signs in the planets and stars. The moon will turn blood red, and one-third of the oceans will turn as red as blood. We have seen that the most unusual sign of the planets, their alignment, occurred in 1986, the same year that the great shooting star, Halley's comet, made its run. But what about turning the oceans and moon blood red?

A lot of scholars maintain that this prophesied blood, death, and destruction will be caused by the atomic war that is going to kill the sailors and fish in the sea and that their blood will turn the oceans red. This is not possible! More blood was spilled in

---

[*]Fatima is discussed in detail in Chapter V.

WWII than will be spilled in WWIII because atomic weapons do not cause bleeding. Victims either vaporize or die of radiation poisoning; they would not pour blood into the sea through cut veins and arteries. Further, not enough blood exists in the world to turn the oceans "blood red."

There is a less popular, but more plausible, explanation of the reddened seas and moon. The fireball comet is a phenomenon somewhat like a sun in brightness and heat. But comets are much smaller, less energetic, and very short lived. A fireball comet starts as a frozen mass that is heated as it approaches the sun. At some point, chemical ignition takes place, and the fireball comet starts to burn, releasing great amounts of its own heat. This differs from common comets, which merely evaporate material that is ionized by the sun to create a bright tail. The fireball comet also has a tail, which can be very hot and may be mostly particles rather than gas. Particles that are thrown off this exploding ball are suspected to be metal oxides, which are often red and poisonous.

Fatima in 1917 and Bayside since 1975 have referred to this future comet as the "Ball of Redemption." Although this is not a pleasant prospect, it is argued that warnings would have to be strong and severe to worry people enough to motivate them to respond. The Ball of Redemption is supposed to be, according to the Bayside message, a three-fold chastisement. Part of that chastisement is that when the Ball of Redemption comes, it will be blinding and that people will be killed, but probably only by fright. It will surely do property damage, and it will perhaps disturb the Earth in several dramatic ways. But, we are not to die from the Ball of Redemption on its first passing. Instead, it is to pass the Earth, travel around the sun, and return to the Earth. On this second trip, one of its larger fragments will collide with the Earth, according to Bayside.

When the Bible has an important message, it repeats it over and over again. Similarly, this warning says that when the Ball of Redemption comes, it will be seen three times. Initially, it will appear in France, rising with the sun, traveling from east to west. This great ball of fire will be witnessed in much of the world, causing many to die of fright. This is the same awe-inspiring experience that people witnessed at Fatima. They were not told at the time exactly what they had witnessed because the event represented was too far in the future. That was 1917, at least 72 years before the predicted event, or it may have been 80 years or perhaps 1,000 years.

The Ball of Redemption, aside from being the source of a hot, blinding light, is also to cause extreme cold and darkness. The dust of its tail not only will cover and poison the surface of the Earth, but also will block out (via space dust) the sun for six days. During these cold six days, the message at Fatima says that not a lamp will light, there will be no light by which to see, and the people will be tormented by unnatural things.* These "things" could be one's conscience, inner feelings, or perhaps inexplicable creations. Everyone will think he or she is about to die and that it is the end of the world. As a result, people will become religious for a week or a month or a year. The religious effect will lose its impact as the shock of the event wears off and as science provides explanations that are not supernatural while assuring all that the phenomenon could not happen again.

If this fireball comet passed close to the Earth or the Earth went through its tail, several inches of dust could land on the Earth. This dust could turn the Earth and the sea red and could coat the moon to appear as red as blood. This heat and poisonous oxide could kill the fish in the sea and could burn and/or kill the trees and grasses. Could this dust cover the Poles? Could this unprecedented heat melt the ice pack at the Poles? Could that in turn trigger the Great Earthquake? Could these events ravage the land, poison lakes and seas, destroy cities through fire and rising tides, and greatly change the Earth's weather? Yes. Furthermore, because of the interdependence of these events, the fireball comet is likely to trigger them all simultaneously.

---

*Ancient history provides a parallel. Before the Great Plague, the whole nation of Egypt went black; not a lamp would light; and no one could see. In that blackness was the torment of unnatural, frightening demons.[F25]

SUMMARY

Keep in mind that the planet Earth and its inhabitants are an intricate part of the cosmos. We are the remnants of distant and ancient dead stars that long ago blew themselves up in supernovas. Throughout its existence, the Earth has been struck by bodies from outer space that have created the continents and the oceans, as well as knocked the Earth off its axis. Many times these impacts have also destroyed most life forms on Earth through dust and Ice Ages.

The Earth is in a very delicate balance, which does not remain unchanged for long geological periods. The impact of eventual sudden changes upon society as we know it is almost unimaginable. The possibility that these changes may not be in the distant future is laid bare by the Bible, Nostradamus, and science itself. But we have examined only physical phenomena in this chapter. Perhaps considering prophecy requires a leap in faith unless we also consider evidence for the existence of a Supernatural Being. The next chapter provides a scientific investigation of this pivotal subject.

V. EVIDENCE OF A SUPERNATURAL BEING: *The Great Pyramid, Dogons, and Fatima*

C an the existence of God be proved scientifically? Can personal bias be restrained and evidence examined and judged objectively as in a court of law? There are reasons to believe that this can be accomplished.

Despite the widespread controversy, there are only two sides to the issue. One camp says that such things cannot be proved scientifically, and the other believes that the existence of God is obvious even without science. Perhaps the scientists who are most capable of developing such proof have not been encouraged to do so. Perhaps they believe that such proof could not be scientific and, so, no serious attempt was ever made.

Perhaps the nonscientific faith believers did not understand how best to apply science and, therefore, could not develop a convincing argument for the existence of a Supernatural Being. Is it possible that after completing 12 to 20 years of scientific study a scientist's "knowledge" and "wisdom" may lead him to feel that science is the solution to everything: that nothing can be above the laws of physics, and nothing can change those physical laws? Therefore, God, as scientists think of Him, cannot exist.

Students are trained to be reluctant to put faith in anything unless it can be substantiated. Science has taught us that physical evidence must be presented to prove a theory. Our justice system is similar; although it will weigh arguments such as motives and intent, it always seeks physical evidence, such as the weapon used or fingerprints. Unfortunately, many people have thought that religion and science are totally opposed because of their seemingly incompatible views. But perhaps we have been avoiding opportunities to find some simple answers.

When we finish looking for all the opportunities to find simple explanations, do we have all the answers? No! But we move closer to the truth. The dividing line for diametrically opposed sides is typically not as obvious as the seam down the center of this book. It is more akin to the separate pages of a book, one on top of the other, which are interrelated and interdependent. Certainly, some ideological problems will always remain, but instead of preconceived enormous separations in positions, we will find that even the most varied dogmas have common ground. Maybe this understanding will make the difference between whether or not we humans can live with ourselves on planet Earth.

Let us examine some lesser known facts that could lend new insights into this deadlocked debate. Common religious rhetoric stating that "I know He is the true God, because He gave me a vision," or "God helped me when I was sick" is not credible to the nonbeliever because it is subjective and cannot withstand scientific scrutiny. Perhaps if we can make a case with strong scientific evidence, we can then talk about not-so-strong evidence and unprovable evidence. Then we can attempt to determine how it may all fit together. Understanding the evidence may give us a wider view of our world, ourselves, and our future. If we keep an open mind, there are answers. The answers may raise further questions, but that outcome does not invalidate the initial answers or evidence.

Seeking proof, some people ask, "If God existed, would He not have left a mark? If God exists, where is He?" Some say He lives in Brooklyn but does not want to get involved. These questions are asked because we would like to think that God exists at our convenience. If there is a Supernatural Being Who has a divine plan, Who is infinitely wise, and so forth, it would seem natural that we, with less experience and knowledge, would not always understand His ways. Still, He could, somehow, let us know if we are barking up the right tree.

For now, consider the argument that if you saw, met, or spoke with God, and then you ever did anything against His law, you would have no excuse. Right now we are allowed to make mistakes because we do not have all the evidence. But what about the evidence we do have? It takes several dramatic forms; we will examine three.

THE PYRAMID OF GIZA

Although Egypt has dozens of pyramids, there is only one Great Pyramid: the Pyramid of Giza. What differentiates the Great Pyramid from the other pyramids? In a word, the Great Pyramid is "perfect." It is also highly symbolic, as discussed later.

From a purely engineering standpoint, consider what makes it unique. First, the Pyramid of Giza is unlike all the other pyramids in its size: It is gigantic. The features are so large that they can be seen from the moon. The structure is 30 times larger than the Empire State Building. Its base covers 13.6 acres (equal to 7 midtown Manhattan city blocks), with each side greater than 5 acres in area. It is the sole remnant of the seven wonders of the world and is the oldest structure in existence. The Great Pyramid is the biggest building ever designed, and it will most likely always remain so. From the equivalent volume contained within it, a highway lane 8 feet wide and 4 inches thick could be built from San Francisco to New York. Just consider all that masonry in one place (see Figure V-1).

All the other pyramids in Egypt are copies of the Great Pyramid. Although the Egyptians have taken credit for building the Great Pyramid, did they design and engineer it? The structure was built before any other pyramid and was started 4,611 years ago. No other pyramid has duplicated its size, construction, meaning, or purpose. The other pyramids were built by Pharaohs, with their great armies of slaves, as tombs for preserving their bodies. As burial sites, pyramids were filled with great treasures for the afterlife, and the structures were monuments to their greatness. The Great Pyramid contains no Pharaoh's body, no treasure chamber, and no treasure. Then what was its purpose? What is its mystery?

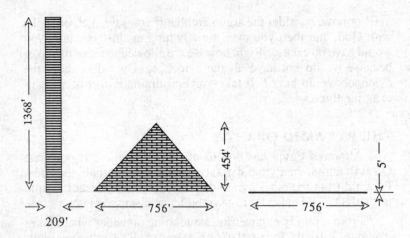

Figure V-1. Twin Tower and Great Pyramid Comparison

The World Trade Center in New York City is the second-tallest building in the world. It is 110 stories high with almost 1 acre of usable office space per floor. It required 11 years for 5,000 men and modern equipment to complete. Each tower used 90,000 yards of concrete, 240,000 square feet of glass, and 80,000 tons of steel. However, if the "empty space" of the Twin Tower were removed so that its density were equal to that of the pyramid's, and if the tower's base were increased to the size of the pyramid's, then the second-tallest building in the world would be only 4 feet 10 inches tall.

Documentaries that explain the pyramids point out that stone quarries not far from the Great Pyramid along the Nile could have been used for building supplies. Although this is valid, it is not a big discovery. The people of the time had tools to cut stone with the precision of that found in the core of the pyramid. Those facts are not what is amazing about the pyramid.

The uniqueness of the Great Pyramid is what was accomplished over 4,600 years ago. For instance, only a solid stone mountain could endure its weight. That is indeed its foundation—a flat, solid granite mountain located just beneath the surface of the ground directly under the pyramid.

To appreciate the location of the 4,600-year-old pyramid, consider how little man knew about the Earth less than 500 years ago. When Columbus sailed to America thinking he was heading to India, man did not even know for sure that the Earth was not flat. Just over 300 years ago, man was still arguing whether the Earth went around the sun or vice versa. Certainly, not knowing the shape of the Earth and all of its continents would signify that map making at the time of Columbus could not have been accurate.

Yet the Great Pyramid is built on the exact center of land mass of the Earth. Further, the pyramid is built to face true north. Actually, the heading is off by 3 minutes of arc. There are 360 degrees in a circle, each made up of 60 minutes. The most accurate observatory ever constructed to locate and measure the North Pole is off by 6 minutes of arc, and it was built much more recently, in the International Geophysical Year of 1957. Apparently, modern science cannot more closely point to the North Pole than the pyramid does. And since the pyramid was built, the North Pole has moved. The pyramid was probably dead on initially, facing due north.

The pyramid's position on Earth is oddly unique in other ways. Its east–west axis corresponds with the longest land parallel across the Earth, passing through Africa, Asia, and America (see Figure V-2). The longest land distance parallel to the equator passes right through the pyramid. Plus, the longest land meridian on Earth, through Asia, Africa, Europe, and Antarctica, also goes exactly through the pyramid. Coincidence? Consider the odds. The Earth has enough land area to provide 3 billion building sites for the pyramid. That produces odds of 1 out of 3 billion for the pyramid to be where it is. Combine that probability with the location of the pyramid on one of the few places on Earth that could actually support its weight—on top of a flat granite mountain. Of course, coincidences do happen.

Another unusual aspect of the pyramid is that its cornerstones have balls and sockets built into them. Since the pyramid is several football fields long, it is subject to heat and cold, expansion and contraction movements as well as earthquakes, settling, and other such phenomena. After 4,600 years, its structure would have been significantly damaged without such construction. Like twentieth-century bridge designs, these balls and sockets allow for expansion and contraction so the pyramid will not self-destruct. The pyramid engineer was wise enough to take that into account 4,600 years ago, before the invention of the spoked wheel.*

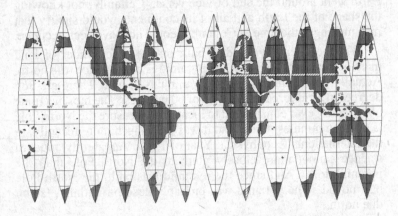

Figure V-2. Location of the Great Pyramid

As shown on a split globe to reduce distortion, the location of the Great Pyramid intersects the Earth's longest land meridian and the longest land parallel.

Was this a lucky accident? Consider how extraordinary it would have been for an Egyptian 4,600 years ago without technological knowledge to anticipate correctly the long-range effects of settling, aging, structural failure, and vibration. If this technology had been known and proved to be effective, why would it take the rest of the world thousands of years, through trial and error, to develop this capability and to design this feature into modern structures? Realizing the need for such engineering and then designing and building the pyramid correctly with no prior studies or experience surely would require an extraordinary amount of good luck.

---

*The first use of a wheel, which was probably a rolling log, is not recorded. The first use of a solid "ox cart" wheel was in circa 3,500 B.C. The spoked wheel as used on Roman chariots appeared around 2,000 B.C., 400 years after the construction of the pyramid.

The pyramid we see today is not the same as it was originally constructed. It presently resembles a pile of rubble (see Figure V-3). The reason for its present appearance, oddly enough, has to do with its being constructed of two very different forms of limestone. The type of limestone that makes up the bulk of the pyramid's core is fairly soft and easy to cut. These 4,000 to 40,000 pound blocks were fitted within the skill of the people of the time. Various methods could have been used to cut, move, and assemble these interior (bulk) stones. This common soft limestone is not immune to attack by the elements—wind, rain, and sandstorm. However, the outer layer of the pyramid was made of a beautifully bright, protective layer of polished stone.

This outer portion of the pyramid is missing because about 600 years ago the so-called casing stones were stolen by the Arabs. Originally, there were 144,000 casing stones to cover the pyramid completely.[37] According to the Bible, 144,000 is the number of Jewish virgins ("...not defiled with women ...without blemish..."), 12,000 from each of the 12 tribes, who are supposed to evangelize the world at the endtime (Rev. 7:2–8, 14:1–5). This armor or breastplate of 144,000 stones may, therefore, have some symbolic significance.

This protective covering was made up of 100-inch-thick, 20-ton blocks of hard, white limestone, which were similar to marble but superior in hardness, and in durability to the elements. The casing stones were so brilliant that they could literally be seen from the mountains of Israel hundreds of miles away. On bright mornings and late afternoons sunlight reflected by this vast mirrored surface of 5-1/4 acres distinguished the pyramid as the only single structure that has ever been visible from the moon.* It was truly a beacon.

---

*In an early space flight, while orbiting the Earth not the moon, astronauts claimed the only structure recognized was the Great Wall of China. That may have been true for that flight path, cloud cover, and viewing schedule. However, the visual resolution of a structure hundreds of feet higher [causing shadowing] and hundreds of feet wider is obvious.

Figure V-3. Original and Present Pyramid

The Great Pyramid did not always look as "rough" as it appears on the right. Originally, it was encased with a layer of tight-fitting, highly polished 20-ton stone slabs. Until these casing stones were stolen, the Great Pyramid more closely resembled the drawing on the left.

The people of the area had viewed the pyramid and its polished stones with awe for centuries. However, it was not until a thirteenth-century earthquake loosened some of these casing stones that the Arabs recognized a great quarry of precut stones that could be used to finish off palaces and mosques.* Since it took centuries to steal all the polished casing stones that were not buried beneath the sand, the pyramid had varying amounts of exposure through the centuries.

---

*The casing stones were used to rebuild the new city of El Kaherah plus Cairo mosques and palaces, including the Mosque of Sultan Hasan. The tumbling of stones from the summit created a 50-foot-high mound of rubble at the base of the pyramid.

Scientists have been able to excavate the sand to see some of the original casing stones and to examine their size, construction, perfection, and precise fit. This study allowed them to project the original size and shape of the pyramid. The original size is important because many discoveries have been made by examining the exact size and shape of the Great Pyramid (see Figure V-4).

Figure V-4 The Original Casing Stone

Although chipped and roughened by the destructive removal of all the elevated casing stones, the size, straightness, placement, and slope of remaining casing stones still can be observed.

The size of these stones is large even by today's standards. When the High Aswan Dam was built in Egypt, for instance, some nonpyramid stonework had to be moved to avoid the rising waters. Stone figures 20 and 50 tons in weight were difficult to move even with heavy cranes and huge modern equipment. Many of the stones had to be cut and reassembled (see Figure V-5).

Placing these stones within even a couple of inches of their nesting place was highly difficult. What is amazing about the outside surface stones of the Great Pyramid is that they are cut within 0.01 (1/100th) inch of perfectly straight and at nearly perfect right angles for all six sides.[*]

Figure V-5. 20-Ton Stones Moved with Modern Equipment

The rising waters of the High Aswan Dam necessitated the movement of some stone treasures of the Great Temple. With modern technology and powered machines, these 20-ton stone slabs could not be positioned as accurately as those placed in the 4,600-year-old Great Pyramid.

---

[*]Such accuracy is equivalent to modern optical quality.

Modern technology cannot place such 20-ton stones with greater accuracy than those in the pyramid.* The pyramid's stones were placed together with an intentional gap between them of 0.02 inch, which means that the blocks were placed with an accuracy better than 0.02 inch. Accuracy of 0.005 inch, which is the thickness of a human hair, is more the norm. Even 4,600 years later, a piece of aluminum foil still cannot be forced between those stones (see Figure V-6). How were 40,000-pound blocks that are virtually square moved within a hair's distance of the next one? What technology was used, and who engineered, designed, and directed the building of this structure?

Figure V-6. Tight Fitting Stones

After centuries of erosion, battering from toppled multi-ton stones, and vandalism, the precision of fit and placement still can be observed. The chipped stone makes the horizontal seam more visible than the less damaged vertical seam pictured above.

---

*The most accurate megamanipulator ever developed was built by Spar Aerospace Limited of Ontario, Canada. Based on a NASA prototype, the hydraulic machine can place 1.25 ton objects with an accuracy of 0.05 inch.

Even more amazing is that the 0.02-inch gap was designed to allow space for glue to seal and hold the stones together. A white cement connected the casing stones and made them water tight. Now, remember, these people could not read or write. They did not yet have the higher forms of hieroglyphics. They did not know why the moon changed its shape, that the brain was the center of thought, or that oxygen was needed for life. They certainly did not have the advantages of twentieth-century chemistry or even the advantages of the limited chemistry of the twentieth-century B.C. In short, they did not have access to advanced technology.

Although these people were uneducated, they managed to come up with an adhesive that is still intact and is stronger than the blocks that it joins. Through 4,600 years of time, settling, earthquakes, fire and flood, some of the stones have cracked, but the cracks stop at the cement. Does that accomplishment seem peculiar?

Whoever built the pyramid used a technology that we still do not possess today to cut, move, and cement stones. Whoever built it also had some knowledge of the Earth, because it was built in the right spot—one of the few places that would support such a great weight. The builder also knew where the greatest land mass of the Earth was in both the north–south and east–west directions. The consequences become more significant as we study the pyramid's units of length.

Measurements

Some specifics deserve explanation, but certain background information is needed first. Do you know why, for instance, the American quart is different in size from the English quart? The reason for the difference is, paradoxically, that our forefathers tried to copy English standards. They decided to adopt their measurement system including the inch, the foot, the yard, the ounce, the quart, and the gallon. Using a bottle to measure volume, they established the standard quart.

The problem was that in those days glass was blown, not molded and, so, there was no inscription on the bottle to label it as a quart. A quart should be a quarter of a gallon. What was thought to be a quart bottle was in fact a fifth. Therefore, it takes four British quarts but five U.S. quarts to make a British gallon. Although we called their fifth a quart, we have fifths also, but everything is exactly 20 percent smaller.*

Our inch also suffers from an inaccuracy in its duplication. As stated by the U.S. Bureau of Standards, the U.S. inch is not the same size as the English inch. As ridiculous as that may seem, it is nonetheless true, albeit the difference is not great or intentional. Measured against the scientific standard, the meter, the British inch is equal to 25.399978 mm, and the American inch is equal to 25.400508001 mm. The differences between standards is greater when the measurement is harder to make, as it is over water. For example, a nautical mile is 6,080 feet in England and only 6,076.1155 feet in America. The conversion factor is 1.0006393, which is correct to the third significant decimal. But the point is that they are not the same.

The reason for their difference is that the standards were based on physical objects. The standard for the inch in America, until about 1960 or so, was a block of platinum in the National Bureau of Standards that was stored under controlled humidity and temperature. When the physical standard for the inch was brought from England over 350 years ago, the temperature-controlled platinum bar did not exist. Today, different means are used for setting standards because measuring a platinum bar accurately is too difficult. Instead the specific orange-red spectrum line of Krypton-86 (wavelength of light) is used in an attempt to establish a nonvariable standard of length. Since England and the United States could not measure the inch exactly, one would expect that others in ancient history trying to "copy" the inch would have had

---

*Before 1824, there were even different gallons. The wine gallon had a volume of 231 cubic inches, the ale gallon had 282 cubic inches, the corn gallon was slightly smaller, and a gallon of flour contained 268.8 cubic inches. (Oddly the first and last are still U.S. standards.)

even more difficulty. However, they were fairly accurate transferring a measure called the sacred Jewish inch.

The sacred Jewish inch (1/25th of a cubit) was used by the original 12 tribes of Israel. Over thousands of years, the Israelites (10 of the 12 tribes, now referred to as the lost 10 tribes) were removed and enslaved by the Babylonians. In captivity, they lost their tradition, religion, and language. When the Israelites became too prolific for the Babylonians (as they were for the Egyptians), they were expelled from Babylon, and they settled in Western Europe, especially the British Isles.

Although the Israelites forgot their heritage, stopped practicing their religion, and took on the ways of "pagans," they did not lose all of their culture. They retained the sacred Jewish inch, which is almost as accurate to the British inch as is the American inch: 1 Jewish inch equals 1.00106 British inches.[*] That is to say, the sacred Jewish inch used 3,000 years ago is just a half of a hair's thickness off from the British inch. The cubit, which is often used in the Bible, is 25 sacred Jewish inches. It is significant that the Jewish inch is not an arbitrary point of measure because it is the major measuring standard for relationships in the pyramid. It is also significant that the English inch is very closely related to the sacred Jewish inch.

To find out more about the "mysteries" of the pyramid, many great scientists have taken thousands of measurements. The accuracy of these measurements was checked hundreds of times by the best methods that could be devised. Even early investigators such as Professor Charles Piazzi Smyth, Astronomer Royal of Scotland, used specially designed wooden scales (metal would change length too much with temperature) to measure distances to 0.001 (1/1,000th) inch and angles to 1 second of arc.[†] All this study has earned the Great Pyramid the distinction of being the most comprehensively surveyed building in the world.

---

[*]This is known by measuring a 1–inch symbol (the only figure engraved in the structure) in the entranceway of the pyramid.

[†]One second of arc is equal to 1/3,600 of a degree, which is equivalent to the angle formed between the top and bottom of a dime 1 mile away.

The measurements showed that the pyramid was designed with great precision. Its casing stones were cut with the accuracy of optical lenses, and even after thousands of years its passages are still straight to 0.013 inch in 100 feet. But what purpose was this unequaled accuracy of construction to serve?

Among others who were intrigued by this question was the great scientist and mathematician Sir Isaac Newton. Newton was attempting to formulate his famous law of gravity* but, to do so, he needed to know the diameter of the Earth. No measurement in the 1600s was accurate enough, especially since Newton theorized that the Earth's spin would cause an equatorial bulge. Hearing of legends claiming that knowledge of the Earth, the past, and the future were contained in the pyramid, Newton set out to investigate. After studying the detailed measurements made by the investigators before him, Newton recognized that many key measurements would be in round numbers if the standard unit of measure was just 0.001 (one thousandth) inch larger than the British inch. This discovery allowed the secrets of the pyramid to be unlocked and revealed unmistakable mathematical relationships.

Some key measurements stand out as highly symbolic. These numbers are repeated in the pyramid over and over again. Recall that the Bible states key points many times as well. Aside from the unique aspects of the pyramid already mentioned, other numerical phenomena stand out. The angle of the sides of the pyramid is not typical, for example. The height and base are not arbitrary. The height of the pyramid's apex is 5,812.98 inches. Each of the sides is 9,131 inches from corner to corner (in a straight line).

From geometry, we know that there is a universal relationship between the diameter of a circle and its circumference. If the circumference of the pyramid is divided by twice its height (the diameter of a circle is twice the radius), the result is 3.14159, which is pi (π). As incredible as that may seem, this calculation is

---

*Newton's law states that the force of gravity is inversely proportional to the square of the distance between two bodies ($F_g = K \cdot M_1 \cdot M_2 \cdot 1/D^2$).

accurate to six digits.* So, the pyramid is a square circle, and thus, π was designed into it 4,600 years ago. Pi is demonstrated many times throughout the pyramid (see Figure V-7).

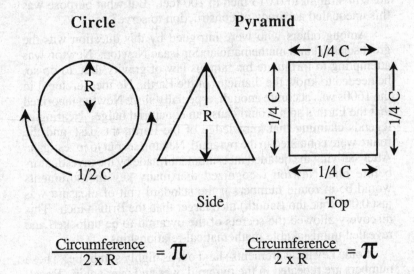

Figure V-7. Geometric Relationships of the Pyramid

Centuries before the development of geometry, or even mathematics and hieroglyphics, the designer of the pyramid seems to have known the value of pi. The periphery of the pyramid divided by twice the pyramid's height is equal to 3.14159, which is pi.

Other numbers are also repeated throughout the pyramid. The length of the pyramid walls when measured as a straight line is 9,131 inches for each of four walls, or 36,524 inches total. At first glance, this number may not seem significant, but move the decimal point (365.24). Then, that dimension can represent slightly less than 365-1/4 days. Modern science has shown us that the exact length of the solar year is 365.24 days, agreeing with the pyramid's number to five significant digits.

---

*The accuracy of π (pi) was known to a greater accuracy only in the sixteenth century when the Dutchman Pierre Metius calculated π to 6 decimal places.

The significance of this symbolic representation is profound. Even today, our calendar is not exactly correct. Every four years we have a leap year, and that would be fine if the year were 365.25 days long. Since it is not, we have to skip leap years in years that end with double zero. Those centennial years do not have a leap year except once every 400 years, when a leap year is put back in to try and make our calendar come out right. Well, somebody knew, thousands of years before it was known by science, that the exact length of an Earth year is 365.24 days.

What is this leading up to? The evidence in the pyramid shows that 4,600 years ago somebody knew a great deal about the Earth. Knowledge of the Earth is demonstrated in other ways. As a result of advances in space science in the mid-1970s, scientists found out something else about the pyramid. The average height of land above sea level on the Earth (Miami being low and the Himalayas being high), as can be measured only by modern-day satellites and computers, happens to be 5,449 inches. That is the exact height of the pyramid. Curious? Is this yet another coincidence? If so, it would be a remarkable coincidence indeed.

Other numbers in the pyramid are symbolic. For instance, about 1940, while examining aerial pictures of the pyramid taken to check certain measurements, a brigadier pilot by the name of Groves noticed something peculiar. The pyramid did not have straight sides; it had concave sides, greatly exaggerated in Figure V-8. The effect cannot be detected by looking at the pyramid from the ground. However, it can be measured with a laser. The pyramid's bow inward is slight but consistent on all sides (see Figure V-6). All of these perfectly cut stone blocks, within a hair's breadth of being exactly straight, had to be made bowed intentionally. But for what possible purpose? That bow is not arbitrary; it is exactly equal to the curvature of the Earth. The radius of this bow is equal to the radius of the Earth.* Another coincidence? Or did somebody leave a message in this structure?

*This radius of curvature is what Newton had long been seeking. By using this measurement (repeated several times in the pyramid's design), Newton was able to complete his theory of gravitation in the 1670s.

Figure V-8. Top View of the Pyramid
Viewed from above, the Great Pyramid's walls bow slightly inward.

With respect to measurements and inches, let us consider the meter. The meter represents science's wise attempt to find a standard length. The meter did not originate with folklore or royal decree, it was carefully planned by scientists from all over the world. Instead of working in arbitrary terms, such as the foot, yard, and mile, which are confusing, they created the metric system to devise a single measure for distance. Units larger and smaller than the meter include the kilometer (1,000 meters), millimeter (0.001 meter), and micrometer or micron (0.000,001 meter).

To eliminate the problems with using a single platinum bar as the universal standard, scientists decided to choose a standard that anyone on Earth could remeasure or recalculate independently. The meter was intended to be 1/10,000,000 of an arc of the Earth that crosses from the equator to the North Pole through a point in Dunkirk, France. Just make this "easy" measurement, and for all time the whole world would be coordinated to this standard, right? The scientists thought so, except for the fact that they have changed its value dozens of times since they set up this standard.

The meter was continuously subjected to differences based on improved measuring techniques. Every year, from satellite, microwave, and other forms of measurements, scientists would discover the value was wrong, albeit only slightly. In fact, what they eventually realized is that measuring the circumference of the Earth from the equator to the North Pole is so difficult that it should have never been attempted. The reason why they cannot make an accurate measurement is that they have to go over so much topography—mountains, valleys, trees, forests, blowing sands, oceans, and tides. In addition, finding the exact North Pole is very difficult. Remember, even modern science in 1957 could not point to the Pole within 6 minutes of arc.

The difficulty in measuring the meter today demonstrates that modern science is still making advances and thus does not have all the answers. Yet the oldest structure on Earth appears to already contain some of the answers sought today.

Examine one more amazing relationship. Multiplying the cubit (25 sacred Jewish inches) by 10 million (the number of meters form the North Pole to the equator) gives the exact distance from the North Pole to the equatorial center of the Earth by a straight line through the Earth. This measurement is easier to make than a curved line over complicated topography and thus is a better standard (see Figure V-9).

The accurate measurement of a topographical arc of the Earth is no longer attempted.* Although science now uses the length of a light wave in a vacuum of a specific excited element (Krypton-86) to measure a meter, the precise measurement of something with such limited length is still very difficult. Optically or geometrically measuring something the size of the Earth and dividing it by 10 million is easy from space and much more accurate. Both modern science and the ancient pyramid used a standard item, the Earth itself, in an attempt to establish a consistent unit of measure.

Whoever built the pyramid had access to information beyond that which earthlings had at that time—at least earthlings as we know them. Now, one can argue that we were visited by scientifically advanced beings from outer space who taught us their technology. That is possible from the evidence presented, perhaps even likely. If so, these advanced beings had the paramount goal to leave behind a message that would endure for eons.

---

*The difficulties of topographical measurement were demonstrated in 1986 when scientists announced that advanced techniques determined Mt. Everest to be only 28,500 feet tall instead of the previously believed 29,000 feet. Thus, Mt. Everest was not the tallest mountain in the world; neighboring Mt. K2 was measured at 28,700 feet above sea level. After a year of investigation, the scientific community was willing to admit that a sizeable correction was required. Contrary to previous beliefs, the summit of Mt. Everest is now thought to be 30,000 feet above sea level.

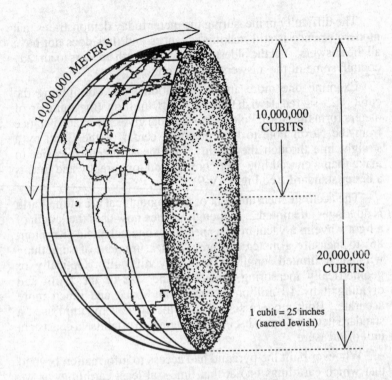

Figure V-9. Measurement of the Earth

The meter was science's attempt to establish a standard unit of length using the Earth as a reference. The meter is 1/10,000,000 of the distance from the equator to the North Pole. The ancient Jewish cubit (25 sacred Jewish inches) has now been found to be 1/10,000,000 of the distance from the center of the Earth to the Pole.

Suppose these beings decided to leave a message. The message would have to be universal yet simple. It would have to survive the centuries and to be understood by all the inhabitants of the Earth despite language and cultural differences. The message would have to be understood by many languages that would not come into existence for centuries after the message was written. The message indicates that whoever built the pyramid knew the Earth well: the length of the year, the radius of curvature, the standard measurement techniques, the average height of the continents, and the center of the land mass. They were able to construct something that we still cannot construct today, and they were able to tie all these things together in this single structure. Were they extraterrestrial or supernatural? The answer is not yet clear. However, so far we have examined only the outside of the pyramid.

To examine the inside of the pyramid, one would normally pass through the single entrance, which was originally fitted with a hinged stone door. This door was a 20-ton stone that fit so precisely that even when the Arabs discovered where it was located and how it was hinged, they could not find it without difficulty.

Aware of treasures found in other pyramids, the Arab Al Manun forced his way into the Great Pyramid in 820 A.D. Finding chisels to be of little value against such a large mass of limestone, his men used the heat of fires and the thermal shock of pouring vinegar over the rock, to fracture the stones. Large battering rams were used to break the fractured stones into removable pieces. Al Manun started his tunneling at the approximate center of the north face, where legend said a passage was hidden. To keep his workers motivated, Al Manun told stories of treasure, but his real interest was the legend claiming that the pyramid contained the past and future history of the world.

As they slowly battered into the pyramid, a stone was heard to fall to the left of their forced tunnel. They dug to the source of the sound, which led them to a descending passage and the entrance door on its far end. They were able to push the door open, but when it closed behind them, they could not reopen it because it fit so perfectly. They had to send somebody back through the excavated hole to push the door open again.

The pyramid entrance is at one end of a 3-1/2-foot-wide, 4-foot-high, Descending Passage (see Figure V-10). At the lower end of the passageway is what has been called the bottomless pit. The falling rock that the Arabs heard was a stone of concealment; if it had not fallen, they would never have located the hidden Ascending Passage. The Ascending Passage rises at the same angle, 26.3°, as the angle of decline of the Descending Passage.

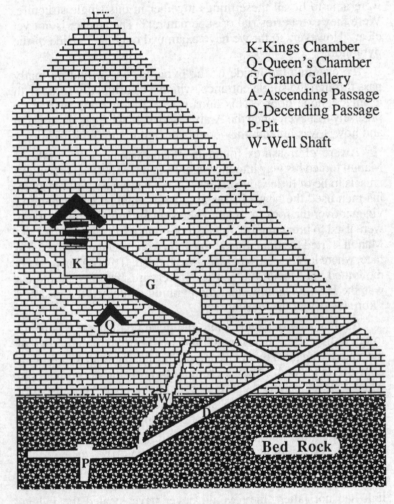

K-Kings Chamber
Q-Queen's Chamber
G-Grand Gallery
A-Ascending Passage
D-Decending Passage
P-Pit
W-Well Shaft

Figure V-10. Pyramid Interior
The inside of the Great Pyramid has two main passages and three main rooms.

The Ascending Passage departs from the Descending Passage and joins with the Main Gallery at the entrance of a room finished in unblemished limestone with a gabled ceiling called the Queen's Chamber.* The Main Gallery also connects with a much larger room finished in highly polished granite having a flat ceiling known as the King's Chamber.† The King's Chamber is covered by five layers of large stone beams. Each 70-ton stone is the equivalent weight of a modern railroad locomotive. These beams hold the pyramid up above the chamber. The King's Chamber is 17 by 34 feet by about 19 feet high.

A crude, steep, twisting crawl space called the Well Shaft connects the lower Grand Gallery with the lower Descending Passage. The passage was hidden by relatively small stone work.

Air ducts in the main chambers keep the year-round temperature comfortable at precisely 68°F. A three-stone red-granite plug at the entrance to the Ascending Passage was wedged in place during the building of the pyramid. This type of granite is rare and identical with that of Mt. Horeb–the mountain on which Moses is alleged to have received the stone tablets with the Ten Commandments. The only way to go beyond the plug was to cut through the softer limestone and bypass the plug.

Now, what is the significance of these structures? First, the Descending Passage happens to line up with the Pole Star. With the door opening so small and the length of the passage 344 feet long, the angle of view is only ± 1/3 of a degree. Because of the slow motion of the stars, the passage lines up precisely to a Pole Star only once every several thousand years. Stars move, and that Pole Star, Alpha Draconis (Dragon Star) has not been in direct

---

*The walls of the Queen's Chamber were mysteriously encrusted with salt 1/2 inch thick. Some have suggested that the salt is the remnant of the Great Flood.

†Within the King's Chamber is an empty coffer made from a solid piece of hard granite. Microscopic analysis revealed that the coffer was formed with a fixed point drill (similar to a modern power milling machine) that used hard jewel bits and a drilling force of 2 tons. How this could have been accomplished 4,600 years ago is not known.

alignment with the Descending Passage for thousands of years. A new Pole Star will finally become perfectly aligned within the next few years; this heavenly body is known as the North Star.

The North Star's proper name is Polaris (like the submarine), which in Greek means "Satan." Each year the Pole Star shines further down the Descending Passage. The North Star will illuminate the entrance to the Well Shaft (sometimes called the point of last escape) in 1997. The North Star will shine on the floor of the Subterranean Passage seven years later in 2004. What is the significance of this event? One can only guess. Is it related to "the sign in the stars" that the Bible mentions with regard to the Second Coming? We can only wait and see. It is, after all, just a matter of time.

Time

The sacred Jewish inch has meaning beyond measurement of distances. The Bible often uses substitutions such as days for years. If we consider the representation of years by inches, the pyramid takes on an entirely new meaning. As a means to record time, the pyramid used stone inches to measure time in years, where 1 inch equals 1 year.

The only scribings in the pyramid, which are in the Descending Passage, depict the year 2141 B.C. This is the year that the last Pole Star was aligned with the Descending Passage. The pyramid was built 4,612 years ago in 2623 B.C. (Since there was never a year zero, an additional year must be subtracted.) One can only postulate what is signified in sacred inches from the entrance of the pyramid to the markings depicting the alignment of the Pole Star—482 inches, thus 482 years later. However, from the point representing building of the pyramid to the point where the Descending Passage meets the Ascending Passage is exactly 1,170 inches, which exactly marks the year of the Jewish exodus from Egypt in 1453 B.C. (see Figure V-11).

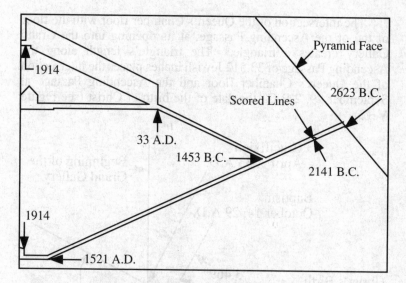

Figure V-11. Chronological Measurements

When years are substituted for inches, the pyramid becomes a prophetic calendar. Dates shown include the alignment of the last Pole Star Draconis (Dragon Star) in 2141 B.C., the start of the pyramid's construction in 2623 B.C., the Exodus of the Israelites from Egypt in 1453 B.C., the death of Christ in 33 A.D., and the start of WWI in 1914.

In all the other pyramids built by the Egyptians, the Pharaoh who directed construction of his burial tomb had his name inscribed over the monument along with other hieroglyphics. There are no Pharaohs' names, no hieroglyphics, no writings at all, and no treasure in the Great Pyramid. Also this structure is the only pyramid to have chambers *above* ground level. From the beginning of the Ascending Chamber to the beginning of the Main Gallery is 1,485 inches. If 1,485 is added to the date of the exodus of the Jews from Egypt (start of the Ascending Passage), the result (if fractions of an inch are taken into account) is April 3, 33 A.D., the crucifixion of Christ and the start of the Main Gallery.

The intersection of the Queen's Chamber floor with the floor of the of the Ascending Passage, at its opening into the Grand Gallery creates a triangle. The triangle's length along the Ascending Passage of 33.512 Jewish inches places the intersection of the Queen's Chamber floor and the Ascending Passage at September 29, 2 B.C., the date of the birth of Christ (see Figure V-12).

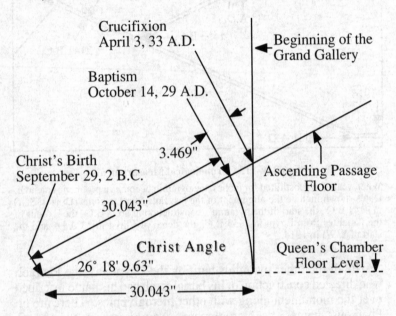

Figure V-12. Christ Angle

The intersection of the Queen's Chamber floor with the floor of the Ascending Passage as it opens to the Grand Gallery creates a triangle depicting the life of Christ in terms of sacred Jewish inches.

Our calendar contains a two-year error. When historians originally attempted to count backward to the birth of Christ, they did so by accounting for the Reign of Kings. One of the kings counted was actually ruler of his country twice, the second time under a different name for a period of two years. When the years of rule were counted, this king's reign was counted twice: once for the total time of his reign and once for the period when he ruled under a different name.[38]

Coincidentally, the horizontal base of the triangle in the pyramid is 30.043 inches, or 3.469 inches short of the crucifixion, which corresponds to the date of October 14, 29 A.D., the date of Christ's baptism. Over 4,600 years ago and over 1,000 years before the first book of the Bible was written, the Ascending Passage exactly depicted in inches (years) and fractions of an inch the exodus of the Jews, and the birth, baptism, and crucifixion of Christ. All that was stored in a stone structure with no written message on it.

In fact, the angle of the Ascending Passage above the horizontal (26° 18' 9.63") can be applied to a map of the area so that a line is drawn 26° 18' 9.63" above the horizontal (east-west) line that bisects the pyramid (see Figure V-13). This line then depicts the beginning and the end of the exodus of the Jews from where they were delivered from the Egyptians at the Red Sea (Reeds Sea) to the crossing of the Jordan River into the Promised Land. This line also passes directly through the town of Bethlehem, the birthplace of Christ. As incredibly precise as this may seem, the pyramid actually pinpoints Christ's birthplace along this line, which could pass through many different villages.

In present-day global navigation, it is recognized that on round surfaces, the shortest distance between two points is part of an arc, and that distance is measured not in feet or inches, but in nautical miles. A nautical mile is approximately 6,076 feet. In old Jewish measurement, a furlong, which is 8,000 Jewish inches, was the equivalent measurement for large distances.

As shown earlier, the pyramid has an astronomically fixed date, which corresponds to the only past alignment of a Pole Star to the Descending Passage. This alignment occurred in 2141 B.C. As shown in the Ascending Passage, Christ was born in the year 2 B.C.—an event 2,139 years in the future of the Pole Star alignment. If we continue to recognize the interrelationship of time and distance, and we measure 2,139 furlongs from the pyramid along the great arc, we would again come to Bethlehem. Thus, the birthplace of Christ is not just a place depicted by a line, but a precise location pinpointed by the intersection of a direction line and a time line that were cast in stone 2,139 years before the event. Obviously, a Supernatural Being would possess the wherewithal to have details work out as planned and would not be prone to great accidents.*

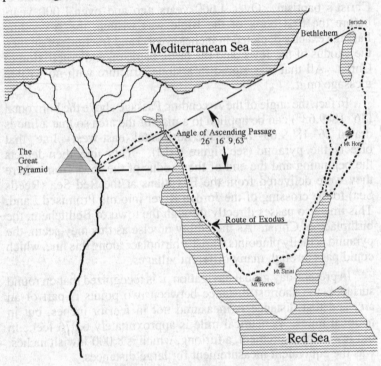

Figure V-13. Pyramid and Bethlehem

When the Christ Angle is superimposed over a map of the Great Pyramid and the Holy Land, the birthplace of Jesus can be identified.

---

*Bethlehem can also be depicted in another significant way. The pyramid casts no shadow at noon on the vernal equinox (the first day of spring or time of rebirth, March 21). When viewing the sunrise from the pyramid on the day of the vernal equinox, one sees the sun (the light) rise directly over Bethlehem (the birthplace of the Son of God).

The Grand Gallery starts in 33 A.D. with the crucifixion. At 28 feet high, it is by far the highest room or passage. The Grand Gallery is 1881-1/3 inches long, and it ends at a horizontal passage that connects to the King's Chamber. Adding 1881-1/3 and 33-1/4 brings us to the year 1914, the start of World War I. It is also 2,520 years after the fall of Assyria in 607 B.C., which started the clock that Daniel prophesied in the Old Testament. He stated (Dan. 9:24–27) that after "seven times period of years" (7 x 360 years because 360 is the number of days in the Jewish year) would be the beginning of "the time of the end." The Bible says that there will be a time of trouble—a worrisome time that will occur after relative peace and tranquillity (not lack of wars and absence of starvation).

We could easily say that the early 1900s saw the birth of aviation, communications, electronics, modern medicine, and all sorts of other things, including WWI, which started in 1914 and ended in late 1918. In 1917 a national home (land) for the Jewish people was reestablished under British control. Before 1917 the Ottoman (Turkish) Empire controlled all the area that we now think of as Israel. Oddly enough, 1917 is 2,520 years (7 x 360) after King Nebuchadnezzar captured Jerusalem in 604 B.C. and led the Jews off to Babylon. In 1917, because of WWI, the British took over Jerusalem and controlled it until the actual independence of the nation of Israel, which took place 29 years later in 1948.

According to Biblical prophecy, the Jewish nation would be reestablished at the end of the allotted time, and it would demonstrate its ability to return to its homeland and regain control of Jerusalem, its holy city. The Biblical prophet Isaias described the event: "as birds flying, so will the Lord defend Jerusalem; defending also He will deliver it, and passing over, He will preserve it" (Isaias 31:5). The Bible further states that the conquering leader will enter Jerusalem on foot.

In 1917 Jerusalem was taken over by British General Allenby, who entered the city on foot. That was a bit unusual because a victorious commander would normally be driven into his captured city. It was also unusual that the Turks fled the city without firing a shot, since they were heavily armed in Jerusalem. The British did not have much in the way of airplanes. But when the British flew their biplanes at treetop level across Jerusalem, they frightened the Turks into flight without ever engaging in battle.

These events fulfilled the two prophecies, the first about the start of the time of trouble (1914 with WWI), and the second about the return of Jerusalem to the Jews in 1917. In fact, the prophecy of Isaias was emphasized by the British before they took Jerusalem in the message hand painted on their planes: The fourteenth bomber squadron of the RAF wrote, "I spread my wings and keep my promise."[39] The date for this time of change or trouble, 1914, was forecasted in the pyramid thousands of years in advance.

There is also strong evidence that the same Isaias who prophesied the reestablishment of the Jews in Jerusalem spoke also of the pyramid: "In that day there shall be an altar to the Lord in the midst of the Land of Egypt, and a monument at the border thereof to the Lord, and it shall be for a sign, and for a witness unto the Lord of Hosts in the Land of Egypt" (Isaias 19:19, 20). In the Hebrew language, each of the original 30 words has a numerical value because each Hebrew letter is also a number. When the 30 words are added up, the total is 5,449, which is one of the most significant (dominant) numbers of the pyramid.[39] It is the exact height of the pyramid in sacred Jewish inches. Although the first books of the Old Testament were written at least 1,000 years after the pyramid was built, the height of the pyramid could not have been measured when the book of Isaias was written, because the geometry required to make such a measurement had not yet been developed. Also, the base of the pyramid was obscured by shifting sand.

What is the relationship? The altar that Isaias refers to *may be* in the King's Chamber of the pyramid, which would be in the center of Egypt at its border. How can it be the center and at the border at the same time? First of all, "Giza" in Egyptian means border or edge, and as shown by a map of Egypt, the pyramid is obviously well inland of its edge. However, the Great Pyramid of Giza is at the edge of the Nile. Second and even more significantly, there were two Egypts. In ancient times before the unification of

Egypt, the wearing of different colored hats signified being Pharaoh of lower (north) or upper Egypt (south).* The borderline between the two Egypts goes right through the pyramid, thus placing the pyramid both in the center and at the border of Egypt.

The Great Pyramid of Giza lives up to its name well. The word pyramid does not define a three-dimensional triangle, nor is its root even Egyptian. The word pyramid is composed of the Greek word "pyra" meaning fire, light, or visible and the Greek word "midos" meaning measures. So, although we have just started to understand the measurements and messages contained within this structure, the Great Pyramid of Giza has been called "the center of measurement and enlightenment (knowledge)" for centuries.

Uniqueness

We have examined many measurements of the pyramid, and it would be only logical to ask if the significance of these measurements could be contrived. After all, one might find his or her birthday or height or age by measuring some point on the thirtieth stone layer along some obscure angle to some arbitrary point in the layers of stone above. However, the measurements of the pyramid are not arbitrary. They are the most obvious details of a geometric figure: its height, length, circumference, length of a passage, and so forth. The measurements were made in sacred Jewish inches (almost the same as our standard inch) and, amazingly, have a profound meaning in both distance and time. Remember, of all the other pyramids in Egypt, not a single one has shown any correlation to any of the measurements taken.

This alone dispels the "contrived matching number" objection. However an even more incredible aspect to the Great Pyramid is that it could not be built or designed by modern science. As requirements are added to a design concept, satisfaction of all

---

*The naming of upper and lower Egypt was based not on an Egyptian recognition of the points of the compass, but rather, on the directional flow of the Nile. Red straw designated the fertile lower delta, and white wool, the upper Nile.

requirements becomes increasingly difficult, or, depending on the requirements, mutually exclusive. For example, it is easy to design a four-sided object, a rectangle, or a rectangle that is twice as high as it is wide. But it is geometrically impossible to draw a rectangle that is twice as high as it is wide and that also has four equal sides. Those separate requirements are mutually exclusive.

Consider just a few of the inflexible requirements facing an engineer in designing the Great Pyramid from scratch (on the Earth or any other planet):

1. The pyramid had to be built where the longest land parallel and the longest land meridian intersect to be at the distinguished location and the center of all land mass.

2. The Pyramid's sides had to have a slope of 51° 51' 14.3" (determined by the latitude of its location) so that at noon on the vernal equinox the pyramid will cast no shadow.

3. The height of the pyramid had to be equal to the average of all land mass above sea level.

So far, all these requirements could be met on most planets provided that the location dictated was not far under water or near the poles (where a structure would always cast a shadow) and that the average land altitude was not miles above sea level). But the requirements become more restrictive. With the height of the pyramid at a fixed value and the sides at a fixed angle, the base and therefore the circumference of the pyramid had to be fixed values. The circumference of the pyramid had to be equal to two times its height times π ($C = 2\pi R$ or $2\pi H$). This is a design requirement that disqualifies designs on all but a miniscule fraction of planets.

With each additional design requirement, the task becomes increasingly difficult or impossible. If the pyramid had to be placed at the center of all land mass, and if the length of its sides had to represent the length of the solar year, a designer would quickly realize that it would be easier to design a planet to fit a specific pyramid then to design a pyramid to meet all of these requirements on a specific planet. Even on Earth it would have been geometrically impossible to design the pyramid with the same interdependencies of the Great Pyramid if a unit of measurement other than the sacred Jewish inch was used. The complex design and interrelationships of the Great Pyramid were possible because the designer had the freedom to choose the unit of measurement that allowed the pieces to be scaled and the interdependencies to fit together.

Thus, the sacred Jewish inch had to be given to the Jews by the designer of the pyramid to allow the structure to be built with all of its interrelated dimensions. The designer of the pyramid had to exercise some direct control of the people of the Earth to use the standard measurement that would one day allow the message to be understood. What is the message?

Suppose we ask the question posed initially: Who built the pyramid? You have to conclude that it was somebody who was very knowledgeable about the Earth and who had technology beyond what we possess today. The builder could also see and/ or, more likely, control the future. The builder knew when and where the most significant person in history was going to be born and when he was going to die and what impact that would have on the people of the Earth. The builder knew thousands of years in advance when wars would be fought and when cities would be reestablished.

Consider the pyramid as a form of proof. Could its builder be a space visitor from another planet? Possibly, if we focus on his advanced knowledge. However, being able to see and/or control the future precisely is what we would recognize as supernatural. Dedication of the interior of the pyramid to the history of the Jews, prophecy, and especially to the life and death of Christ indicates that this last event is the most significant event to occur on Earth. This is not only evidence for the existence of a Supernatural Being, but also evidence that this Supernatural Being recognizes the significance of religion.

The pyramid is "hard" evidence of a Supernatural Being left in stone. Evidence of a different form comes from a remote tribe in Africa.

THE DOGON TRIBE

In a remote part of western central Africa lives a Stone Age group of people called the Dogon tribe. The Dogon's level of technology peaked at spear making, grass hut building, and group hunting. In a cultural sense, they are also Stone Age in many of their rituals and religious beliefs. They are literally in the Stone Age for not having yet developed metallurgy or even crude forms of other sciences.

The Dogons first became noteworthy to the Western World at about the turn of the seventeenth century, when missionaries attempted to convert them to Christianity.[38] The missionaries found them unique in several respects, one of which was the ease of converting them to Christianity. This task was easy because of the similarity of Christianity to their own religion. The Dogons had believed that God sent His Son to mankind to teach them the errors of their ways, but that mankind did not recognize Him and hung Him on a tree. This totally isolated civilization had practiced this belief for as long as their history could record and well before meeting any Christians.

The missionaries certainly exploited that similarity to Christianity. They also recorded other peculiarities about the Dogon religion. The Dogons had worshipped a star that they believed was the residence of God, the center of life, and the center of the universe. They would point to the place in the sky where this star is positioned. But this star cannot be seen because it is located relatively near a rather bright star known as Sirius. The Dogons maintained that this special star revolves around Sirius once every 50 years. They further contended that the path of revolution is not circular, but elliptical, with the major axis being 2-1/2 times the minor axis.

Although these beliefs interested the missionaries, they had no means at that time to prove or disprove them. However, advances in science in 1862 allowed investigators to substantiate another star close to Sirius named Sirius B.[1] How did the Dogons know about this star, which was not visible from Earth until the development of powerful telescopes?

In the twentieth century, science again increased technology to the point of recognizing wobbles in distant stars. These wobbles were analyzed by computers to determine that they were caused by other large bodies in orbit about them. It was determined that Sirius B was revolving about Sirius, as the Dogons have maintained throughout their history. Further investigations through subsequent years established that the period of revolution of Sirius B about Sirius A is, to the best estimation, 50.1 years. Within just the last several years, refinement of computerized data and other advanced techniques have established that the orbit of Sirius B is elliptical, with a major to minor axis ratio of 2-1/2 to 1.

This is an overwhelming set of coincidences. The tenets of the Dogon religion, later substantiated as scientific facts, could not have been given to the Dogons by any earthling because the technology to derive this information did not exist then. Is this to be considered as evidence that God lives on Sirius B? No, that is not the intent. However, it does suggest that someone managed to impress upon the Dogons a religious message about a Godly existence and a Godly visitation as well as a knowledge of the universe, which until recent times could not have been known with such detail. The evidence for an information transfer from a knowledgeable, unearthly source is obvious. It is significant that this source also taught the existence of a Supernatural Being.

One more type of evidence substantiates the existence of a Supernatural Being.

FATIMA

Throughout the world, there have been many visitations, hallucinations, wishes, and fabrications about supernatural beings giving messages or performing incredible feats. Fatima is a modern-day event named after a small Portuguese village. The 1917 event has almost been forgotten. The Catholic Church is the only organization that officially recognized Fatima, and yet 97 percent of adult Catholics are not familiar with Fatima.* Fatima is

*The investigation of Fatima was conducted without the author being Catholic or having any denominational bias.

presented here not because of its messages, but because of the large number of people who witnessed the event: 71,000. Normally, a dozen or two dozen people or a hundred people witness an aberration or claim to have received a miraculous cure.

In the story of Fatima, a special messenger of God visited three small children 7 to 10 years old in Fatima, Portugal. As in other visitations, these children were poor and uneducated. When visitations are made to less affluent, less educated people, they cannot be accused of being so learned or clever as to deceive the parties who are attempting to investigate what may have taken place.

As these visitations occurred, the local dictatorship was trying to abolish religion to increase control over the people. Therefore, the government had committed itself to a major program to close down churches. After hearing about their claims, the mayor had these three children arrested. He threatened them with torture in an attempt to stop them from telling this terrible lie about a woman who glowed, stood on a tree and gave them messages. But they refused to change their story. As a result of public outcry, the children were released and they became more popular. Thousands of people came from miles around to be present at prescheduled apparitions. Some claimed to see a light, some say that they saw the tree limb bend, but most could see nothing except these children in a peculiar state of mind, which can be called a hypnotic trance or ecstasy.

When other apparitions have appeared (dozens of similar cases are well documented), incredible happenings have occurred. People experiencing ecstasy were able to kneel on stones and not feel pain or to have lighted matches put on their flesh without recognition, flinching, or harm. For example, nuns were persecuted and tortured by the Russians for not complying with the work requirement dictated by the State. They were left for 16 hours a day in freezing weather without proper clothing. The nuns came back from this daily ordeal without a sniffle or a cold and without any pain. Each day they would just kneel in ecstasy, watching a vision that told them their oppressors would become frightened and would give up and that their ordeal would strengthen religion in Russia.

Fatima differs from these other apparitions in what it did. The vision told these three children many things, all of which came true. It said that two of the three children were going to die soon and that one was going to live for a long time. Lucy, the third child, is still a nun in the Catholic Church. The children were instructed by these visions to tell everyone that on Friday, October 13, 1917, there would be a great miracle and a sign to let the people know that the messages were true.

The most startling message received was that WWI would soon end. But within the space of 25 years, a much worse war would engulf the world unless people adhered to the teachings of God. It also said that unless these changes took place immediately, there would be a great famine and plague throughout Europe, that there would be nothing on the vine to eat. Further, the message claimed that Russia would scatter her errors throughout the world.

As proclaimed, a great plague occurred: More people died from the flu in 1918–1919 than were killed in WWI.[*] In 1917 many Americans and Europeans wore sterile face masks in stores and on trolleys in an attempt to stop spreading this influenza. There were no shots for the flu at the time; people became weakened, spread the disease, and died. The prediction of the Communist threat to the world was made in the same year that later witnessed the Russian Revolution and the rise of Communism. At the time of the prediction, Russia was still a weak, unstable nation, which was a threat to no one, let alone the world.[†] A vine fungus later spread through Europe for 3-1/2 years and left no grape unspoiled. Of course, 25 years did not pass between the end of WWI in 1917 and the start of WWII in 1939.

---

[*]From 1918 to 1919, 20 million people died of influenza, 850,000 of whom were Americans.

[†]The five-month visitations witnessed by the children of Fatima in 1917 warned of the "spreading of errors from Russia and a great war." The messages of Fatima correspond exactly with the Russian Revolution. In May the Tsar abdicated, and in October (old calendar) the Democratic Provisional Government was overthrown by the Bolshevik Revolution. At the same time, the Christian Russian nation was forced to atheism, and the country started on its course of world domination.

The message also said that in the latter half of the second half of the twentieth century, a great, fantastic war would engulf the world. No one would survive this war, save the intervention of God, unless mankind adhered to the teachings of the Lord. That was the message. No one saw the aberration or received the message except for three young, uneducated children. So, why should anyone believe this message?

The day of October 13 was rainy, with mud six inches deep through the fields at Fatima. A crowd of 71,000 people gathered, among them hundreds of representatives from the media. As noon approached, the aberration began as thousands of people stood in mud up to their ankles. Lucy, the only one of the three children to survive the next two years, turned to the crowd and stated that the Lady of the vision had asked all to put their umbrellas down. Closing the umbrellas after the long walk through muddy, windy fields meant that everyone was wet and soiled. Soon after, the cloud cover broke, and the sun could be seen.

Lucy pointed to the sky so that all would look up. Suddenly, the sun did something strange. It turned different colors and started whirling brilliantly and rapidly, throwing out fireballs in all directions as it came crashing down to Earth, seemingly on a speeding collision course. This vision continued for more than three minutes, with the sun growing closer, bigger, brighter, hotter, and more furious. The 71,000 people went almost insane, diving to the ground, covering their heads and thinking they were all about to die as this was the end of the world. Everyone present saw the Earth and sun about to collide.

After this three-minute vision, the sun went back to its original position. Just as the crowd started to get up off the ground, the sun repeated the phenomenon. It turned every color of the rainbow, spun at tremendous speeds throwing out fireballs in every direction, and came crashing down to Earth. Just before it hit the Earth, when all thought that they were going to succumb to the heat, the sun went back to its former position. And, just in case anybody missed it, the sun performed this spectacle a third time.

The total time this vivid vision was seen by 71,000 people was 12 minutes. When the fireball finally rose back to its normal position and became the sun again for the third time, everyone got up off the ground. Quite unexpectedly, they were not only dry (perhaps from the great heat), but also unsoiled. The ground was solid, and there was no mud on their shoes, bodies, or clothes. Lucy said that this was the sign sent to make them believe the message.

This story was carried by major newspapers throughout the world, with the greatest coverage presented by the normally government-controlled and predominantly anti-religious Portuguese papers, *The Daily News* and the *Century*.* But outside of Portugal, it was given coverage for only one day. Soon everyone forgot about the vision, the warning, and the prediction.

How often do we hear someone say, "If there is a God, why does He not give us a message to tell us what to do?" Well, messages have been given. Maybe people do not like to be told; maybe people do not want to hear frightening or unpleasant predictions, such as the coming war and the next war after that. Maybe people do not want to hear about giving up what they are doing and being more righteous. Maybe people do not like the evidence, and so they reject it and say there is no acceptable evidence.

There are other examples of strong evidence, such as the picture of Guadeloupe, and the aberrations of Garabandal, but they would be repetitive and would add little to the basics already established.

---

*"...then the silvery sun, still shrouded in that grayish light, began to rotate and wander within the circle of the receded clouds! The people cried out with one voice. Thousands, transported by ecstasy, fell to their knees upon the muddy ground. Then, as if it were shining through the stained glass windows of a great cathedral, the light became a rare blue, spreading its rays upon the nave....Yellow spots were falling now upon the white kerchiefs and dark shirts of coarse wool. They were spots which repeated themselves indefinitely over the landscape. All the people were weeping and praying bareheaded, weighted down by the greatness of the miracle. These were seconds, moments, that seemed hours...." *The Daily News* (October 14, 1917).

A TRIANGLE OF EVIDENCE

The Great Pyramid is a physical, concrete piece of evidence contained in the oldest, largest monument on Earth. It demonstrates superior *scientific knowledge* with the unearthly ability to "see" or control the future thousands of years in advance. In symbolic terms, the pyramid indicated that the single most important event to occur in the next 4,600 years was to be the life of Christ. The pyramid contains evidence not only for a Supernatural Being, but also for One Who recognizes the *importance of religion* (see Figure V-14).

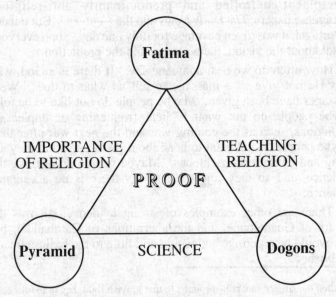

Figure V-14. Triangle of Proof

The evidence for the existence of a Supernatural Being is graphically represented. The Great Pyramid, the Dogon Tribe, and the story of Fatima, Portugal, present scientific evidence of divine purpose. Each area of evidence displays two of the three forms of proof presented, which reinforces the two remaining areas of evidence.

As with the pyramid, the first point of credibility of the Dogons is *science*. The major difference is that instead of merely recording religious events, the Dogon visitations *taught religion* in terms of Who God is and what was the mission of His Son. The Dogons demonstrate evidence for a Supernatural Being dedicated to religion, that is, "God."

Fatima completes the triangle. Fatima is also explicit about the future, but instead of supplying scientific and physical evidence, it provided miraculous visions to 71,000 eyewitnesses. The key message of Fatima is clear: Mankind must do as God commands or suffer the punishment predicted in the message. Thus, Fatima demonstrated that the Supernatural Being not only recognizes the *importance of religion* and God, but also *teaches religion* and, in fact, proclaims to be God.

In view of all the scientific evidence, control of the future, and miraculous visions, can you "beyond a shadow of a doubt" reject such a claim?

VI. CONCLUSION:
Facing the Future

T he investigation began with prophecy to demonstrate that the crucial period we are entering has been foreseen and anticipated for centuries. Based on the most modern techniques of science, the predictions made are not only plausible, but likely. The evidence suggests that at best the major forces that maintain our society hang in precarious balance. At worst our environment, economic system, military balance, and society at large are distended for major alterations that will cause catastrophic changes throughout the world.

UPSETTING THE BALANCE

How will these precarious forces interact? The most common scenario is one of all-out nuclear war. According to widespread belief, such a war would completely destroy all life on Earth.* However, other catastrophes, which could be triggered without a nuclear exchange, can destabilize society's delicate balance. Even small, seemingly unimportant skirmishes located in remote locations of the world can have an avalanche effect. For example, in the Iran-Iraq war, which endured for over seven years, neutral ships were attacked as belligerent nations attempted to damage their opponent's

---

*This outcome exaggerates man's scientific capability. An H-bomb could kill the population of the world only if all 5-billion inhabitants were located in an unprotected 3,000-square-mile area. Although a full-scale nuclear exchange would leave few cities standing in the United States, Russia, and Europe, 100-million to 300-million people would survive, in suburbs and farming communities. Even after fallout takes its toll, the population of the Earth would be about 3 billion people 90 days after the war started.

economy. As the effect on international shipping increased, the West provided a greater military presence to protect its interests.*

Interruption of oil flow would cause oil prices throughout the world to rise, and that in turn would cause inflation. Nations struggling to check growing inflation would be forced to raise interest rates to reduce consumption of all goods. But higher interest rates would also prohibit Third World nations from making even token payments on their overwhelming debts. Thus, they would be held in default. Such a widespread circumstance could only result in the total collapse of the economic system of the West.†

As a consequence of multiple instabilities and their complex interdependencies, it is equally possible that the same catastrophic effects could occur from the opposite direction.

Changes in the environment caused by man, earthquakes, or cosmic encounters such as asteroids, meters, or comets could also collapse world economics. Even a small temperature variation across the Earth could change wind or weather patterns by moving the jet stream. Likewise, destruction of the ozone layer or the obstruction of sunlight would have overwhelming effects on the ability to produce enough food for the world's population. An altered global weather system can produce many drought areas more severe than that recently experienced in Africa. Unfortunately, such hardships most often are accompanied by starvation and plague.

Even the United States could revert to the Dust Bowl Era of 55 years ago. As a result, food would become very dear and

---

*The logic of this action is not obvious since America instigated the formidable military buildup, but U.S. ships and oil were not at jeopardy.

†A truly delicate balance exists here. Peace in the area of the Persian Gulf could lead to an extension of the oil glut, which could depress prices to less than $10 per barrel (as it did for a brief period in 1987). Low oil prices may seem beneficial to many world economies, but the oil-producing nations, many of which are Third World countries, would no longer have the export values to generate the capital necessary to make payments on their international debts. Thus, the world would still suffer economic collapse.

difficult to obtain. Starvation and malnutrition would become commonplace. Farms would fail at an unprecedented rate, dwarfing the record rate of farm failures in America today. Banks, especially those in the farm belt, would be devastated. As banks collapsed, people would lose faith in the banking industry. The gross national product, trade balances, and unemployment would all be affected. This economic situation would extend to other areas of the world, causing nations that are barely able to survive in relatively good times to default on loans. As a result, banking in the West would collapse, destroying the world's economy.

What happens to society, when economics and food distribution become uncontrollable? Historically, such circumstances lead to revolts or war. War serves as a diversion, and it can be promoted as the solution. War reduces the population and may result in the possible gain of productive lands, but only at the expense of the vanquished.

An economic turmoil that causes banks to collapse and loans to be called would shut down many businesses and farms. Consequent shortages of jobs, housing, and food would contribute to famine and plague. Such drastic conditions precipitate political instability and war.

Can economic problems really bring about war? They already have! Just before WWII, most nations (except the United States) had large international debts, as they have today.

The 1929 stock market crash in New York caused a panic withdrawal of funds from Europe, which in turn caused the largest bank in Austria to collapse. European banks called in foreign assets to compensate for funds tied up in Austria. This recall of assets tightened money availability to the point that nations were unable to maintain their international loan payments—mostly due to the United States.

In 1930 Brazil, Bolivia, Peru, Chile, Ecuador, and Colombia all announced suspension (permanently) of foreign loan payments. In 1931 Hungary, Yugoslavia, Rumania, Poland, Bulgaria and Mexico all defaulted.

Countries were forced off the gold standard to allow printing of valueless money. Nations had borrowed funds based on the collateral of IOUs they held from another country–Germany. Because the war debt from WWI caused austerity measures (not unlike those of present Third World debtors) that were destroying the German economy, Germany also declared nonpayment of its international debt in 1931. Without the German "assets" and payments, England, France and Italy defaulted on their loans to the United States.[*] As a consequence of this financial chaos, tensions ran high, economies were destroyed, and revenge was sworn. Desperate people without jobs brought to power a dictator promising change, and the world entered its second world war.

Unfortunately, the speed at which war can be enacted is almost instantaneous. No longer does war require months for mobilization; war on a grandiose scale can be launched by the press of a button. Whether by accident, miscalculation, misunderstanding, or madness, warfare on an unthinkable scale may be initiated. Once started, it would be unlikely to be restrained from global escalation, culminating in the use of thousands of multi-megaton warheads. Not only would these weapons have the obvious military effects—destruction of population, cities, farms, and industry—but also they would destroy the environment through fallout and nuclear winter dust generation. Thus, even nonwarring continents would be burdened with environmental and economic catastrophes.

---

[*]Not a penny of these debts has ever been reinstated or paid back, not even by Great Britain or France.

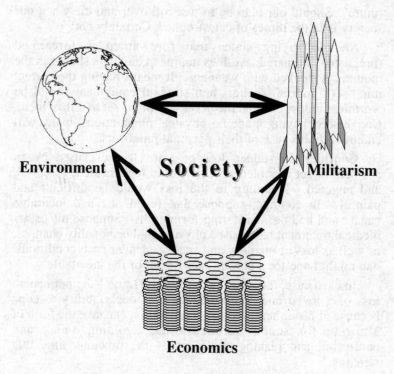

Figure VI-1. Interdependent Forces in Society

Economic pressures determine military spending and environmental safeguards. A change in the environment can cause economic strife, which has in the past led to war. Even limited warfare may have irreversible environmental impacts, which in turn have devastating economic consequences.

Dealing with Eventualities

What can you do? Even if you were the President of the United States, little could be done except to push back the inevitable economic collapse or major military conflict. The forces threatening economic and military upheaval are too well entrenched to be delayed for long, and global natural disasters cannot be affected by any human action. Then do we ignore our future? Should our plan be to just roll over and die when our society is in the throes of catastrophe? Certainly not!

An old saying states that forewarned is forearmed (prepared). Preparedness does not mean having a shelter in the mountains stocked with weapons. It means having the correct mind-set. Indeed, shelters and survival equipment would be worthless unless one had the necessary mind-set to utilize them. Conversely, having made no physical preparations, many will endure only because of their personal mind-sets.

Consider the sudden loss of a loved one caused by an accident or act of violence. One would feel cheated, bereaved, and angered. Adapting to the loss would be difficult and painful. In contrast, suppose that loved one had incurable cancer and had been suffering for months. Suppose his or her medical treatment had caused physical and personality changes, as well as loss of memory and speech. Under such conditions, one might hope for a prompt conclusion of the inevitable.

In each case, the result is exactly the same—the permanent loss of a loved one. The difference is one's ability to cope because of his or her mind-set. Preparation can take the form of allowing for sound rationalization, avoiding shock and confusion, and making the most of the precious time that remains.

One could say that the world's society has a terminal disease. The right mind-set is not to ignore the prognosis, but to make the most of the time that remains. Emotional and spiritual preparation will help us to overlook the imperfections of each "normal" day and to cope with abnormal days as they approach.

If we can accept prophecy and the scientific evidence of the instabilities of our society, then we should find consolation in inevitability and in the confirmation of the existence of God. For then there is a plan, events are not out of control, and we have hope. Whether that hope manifests itself as belief in the rapture, divine protection, or in the rewards of a hereafter, it encourages us to endure. Although we cannot prevent the approaching catastrophes, we can be wise enough to recognize that the preordained events that have been prophesied since ancient times are likely to soon occur. We may also realize that procrastination of our preparation until our future is upon us can be an unreconcilable mistake.*

The global impact of upcoming events can be found in the warning of Joel (2:28–32), written 3,000 years ago. His message only now takes on a comprehensible meaning:

Your sons and daughters shall prophesy,
Your old men shall dream dreams,
Your young men shall see visions...
And I will work wonders in the heavens and on the Earth,
Blood, fire, and columns of smoke;
The sun will be turned to darkness,
And the moon to blood,
At the coming of the Day of the Lord,
The great and terrible day.

---

*As stated in Matthew 24; 37–39, "For as in the days before the flood they were eating and drinking, marrying and giving in marriage until the day when Noah entered the ark, and they did not understand until the flood came and swept them all away..."

Letters to the author are welcome
and should be addressed to;

John Zajac
P.O. Box 21237
San Jose, CA 95121

REFERENCES

1. *The New Encyclopædia Britannica* (Encyclopædia Britannica Inc., Chicago, Illinois, 1987).

2. Anthony Sherman, "Washington's Visions," *The National Tribune* (December 1880).

3. Charles Neilson Gattey, *They Saw Tomorrow* (George G. Harrad & Co., London, England, 1977).

4. Erika Cheetham, *The Prophecies of Nostradamus* (Perigee Books, New York, New York, 1973).

5. Spencer Crump, *Ride the Big Red Cars—The Pacific Electric Story* (Trans-Anglo Books, Glendale, California, 1983).

6. Peter Collier and David Horowitz, *The Rockefellers an American Dynasty* (Holt, Rinehart and Winston, New York, New York, 1976).

7. Patti Hassler, "Clang, Clang, Clang, Went the Trolley," *60 Minutes*, Columbia Broadcasting System (December 6, 1987).

8. Charles R. Ashman, *Kissinger—The Adventures of Super-Kraut* (Lyle Stuart, Inc., Secaucus, New Jersey, 1972).

9. *New York Times* (November 19, 1987).

10. *Washington Times* (June 3, 1987).

11. Tom Parker, *In One Day* (Houghton Mifflin, Boston, Massachusets, 1985).

12. "At CitiCorp, a Glimpse of the Future," *U.S. News & World Report*, p. 54 (July 9, 1984).

13. Stanley N. Wellborn, "Big Brother's Tools Are Ready, But...," *U.S. News & World Report*, p. 88 (January 2, 1984).

14. Robert L. Preston, *How To Prepare for the Coming Crash* (Hawkes Publishing, Salt Lake City, Utah, 1975).

15. David Webber and Noah Hutchings, *Computers and the Beast of Revelation* (Huntington House, Inc., Shreveport, Louisiana, 1986).

16. Alan Stang, "Abolish the Fed," *American Opinion* (April 1985).

17. Congressman Louis McFadden, *Congressional Record*, June 15, 1933.

18. Monroe W. Karmin, "Risky Movements in the Money Markets," *U.S. News & World Report* (March 2, 1987).

19. *666 Is Here* (Today in Bible Prophecy, Inc., Huntington Beach, California).

20. *Blanchard Bulletin*, James U. Blanchard & Company, New Orleans, Louisiana (August 20, 1984).

BIBLIOGRAPHY

Arenson, K. W., "A Debt of $1 Trillion: Its Effect on Economy," *New York Times* (September 30, 1981).

Bail, Eli, *From Rail to Freeway* (Interurban Press, Glendale, California, 1984).

Cassidy, Robert, *Margaret Mead—A Voice for the Century* (Universe Books, New York, New York, 1982).

Cheetham, Erika, *Nostradamus 1985 and Beyond* (Perigee Books–Putnam Publishing Group, New York, New York, 1985).

Cheetham, Erika, *The Prophecies of Nostradamus* (Perigee Books–Putnam Publishing Group, New York, New York, 1973).

Coleman, John, *The Club of Rome, The Enemy of Mankind* (Christian Defense League, Arcadia, Louisiana, 1983).

Collier, Peter, and David Horowitz, *The Rockefellers* (Holt, Rinehart and Winston, New York, New York, 1976).

Connor, Edward, *Prophecy for Today* (Tan Books and Publishers Inc., Rockford, Illinois, 1984).

El-Baz, F., *"Desert Builders Knew a Good Thing When They Saw It"* (Smithsonian, Washington DC, April 1981).

Fritz, N. H., Jr., "Clausewitz and U.S. Nuclear Weapons Policy," *Air University Review* (November-December 1982).

Haffert, John M., *Meet the Witnesses* (International Press, Washington, New Jersey, 1961).

Hogue, John, *Nostradamus and the Millennium* (Doubleday and Company, Inc., Garden City, New York, 1987).

Holy Bible (Catholic Book Publishing, New York, 1957).

Hughes, Patrick, "1816–The Year Without a Summer," *Weatherwise* (June 1979).

Johnston, Francis, *Fatima* (Tan Books and Publishers Inc., Rockford, Illinois, 1980).

Leoni, Edgar, *Nostradamus and His Prophecies* (Bell Publishing Co., New York, 1982).

Lindsey, Hal, *The Late Great Planet Earth* (Bantam Books Inc., New York, New York, 1981).

Lindsey, Hal, *There's a New World Coming* (Vision House, Santa Ana, California, 1974).

Muller, Richard, *Nemesis the Death Star* (Weidenfeld & Nicolson, New York, New York, 1988).

Murray, Richard, *The Key to Nostradamus* (Scorcap Publishing Co., Cleveland, Ohio, 1975).

Our Lady of Fatima (Catholic Treasuries, Montana, California, 1982).

Raymond, E., *The Great Pyramid Decoded* (Artisan Sales, Thousand Oaks, California, 1978).

Ripley's Believe It or Not, American Broadcasting Company (1985).

Rivers, Gayle, *The War Against the Terrorists* (Charter Books, New York, New York, 1987).

Roberts, Henry C., *The Complete Prophecies of Nostradamus* (Nostradamus Company, Oyster Bay, New York, 1980).

Roberts, J. M., *The Mythology of the Secret Societies* (Charles Scriber's Sons, New York, New York, 1972).

Taylor, Charles, *World War III* (Thomas Nelson, New York, New York, 1979).

The Concise Oxford French–English Dictionary (Oxford University Press, New York, New York, 1980).

Tompkins, Peter, *Secrets of the Great Pyramid* (Harper & Row, New York, New York, 1978).

Von Daniken, Erich, *Chariots of the Gods?* (G. P. Putnam's Sons, New York, New York, 1970).

Webber, David, and Noah Hutchings, *Computers and the Beast of Revelation* (Huntington House, Inc., Shreveport, Louisiana, 1986).

White, John Wesley, *WWIII* (Zondervan Books, Grand Rapids, Michigan, 1981).

Wilson, C., *Starseekers* (Doubleday and Company, Garden City, New York, 1980).

"Year Without a Summer," *American History Illustrated* (June 1970).

Index